PROBLEMS
IN
MACHINE DESIGN

PROBLEMS
IN
MACHINE DESIGN

BY

O. A. LEUTWILER, M. E.

PROFESSOR OF MECHANICAL ENGINEERING DESIGN, UNIVERSITY OF ILLINOIS
MEMBER OF THE AMERICAN SOCIETY OF MECHANICAL ENGINEERS
MEMBER OF THE SOCIETY OF AUTOMOTIVE ENGINEERS
AUTHOR OF "ELEMENTS OF MACHINE DESIGN"

FIRST EDITION
THIRD IMPRESSION

McGRAW-HILL BOOK COMPANY, Inc.
NEW YORK: 370 SEVENTH AVENUE
LONDON: 6 & 8 BOUVERIE ST., E. C. 4
1923

COPYRIGHT, 1923, BY THE
MCGRAW-HILL BOOK COMPANY, INC.

PRINTED IN THE UNITED STATES OF AMERICA

THE MAPLE PRESS - YORK PA

PREFACE

The best known text books on the subject of machine design, do not contain a sufficient number of problems, the solution of which will familiarize the student with the application of theory and at the same time give him a better working knowledge of the subject. The purpose of the author, in preparing this book, has been to provide a series of isolated problems covering the various parts of the subject of machine design. Practically all of the problems are taken directly from existing machines; hence the student is working with actual engineering information and not with hypothetical data chosen at random. Problems of the latter type frequently lead to absurd results, thus causing the student to lose interest in the work.

The majority of the problems, included in Sections I to XV, deal with simple isolated machine parts, which are treated independently and, in general, have no connection whatsoever with machine parts discussed in other problems. Section XV includes problems in the solution of which the student makes a complete force and stress analysis of all the elements used in the machine, thus showing the relation existing between the various elements used in building up a complete machine.

Problems taking up the design of simple machines are given in Section XVI. Some of the statements are in the form of specifications and it is hoped that the material included in this section will aid the teachers of machine design in placing before the student a clear and concise statement of the problems to be solved. Each specification is accompanied by the necessary data pertaining to a series of sizes of the machine covered by the specification. Section XVII contains a number of tables that may be found useful in connection with design work.

The references to articles, figures and equations given in a number of the problems, refer to the author's text book on Machine Design.

O. A. LEUTWILER.

URBANA, ILL.,
January, 1923.

CONTENTS

	PAGE
PREFACE	v

SECTION
- I. STRESSES AND STRAINS IN MACHINE PARTS 1
- II. RIVETED CONNECTIONS 8
- III. BOLTS AND SCREWS. 19
- IV. COTTER AND PIN CONNECTIONS. 27
- V. CYLINDERS, PLATES AND SPRINGS. 29
- VI. BELTING 35
- VII. ROPE TRANSMISSION 41
- VIII. CHAIN TRANSMISSION. 48
- IX. FRICTION TRANSMISSION. 56
- X. SPUR GEARING. 63
- XI. BEVEL AND SCREW GEARING. 68
- XII. COUPLINGS AND CLUTCHES. 76
- XIII. BRAKES. 85
- XIV. SHAFTING AND BEARINGS 93
- XV. GENERAL PROBLEMS 105
- XVI. DESIGN PROBLEMS 118
- XVII. TABLES. 129

PROBLEMS IN MACHINE DESIGN

SECTION I

STRESSES AND STRAINS IN MACHINE PARTS

1.—The symmetrical link, shown by the dotted lines in Fig. 1, transmits a force P having a magnitude of 16,600 lb. (*a*) Determine the dimensions t and b_1 of the body of the link, assuming the permissible tensile stress is 10,000 lb. per square

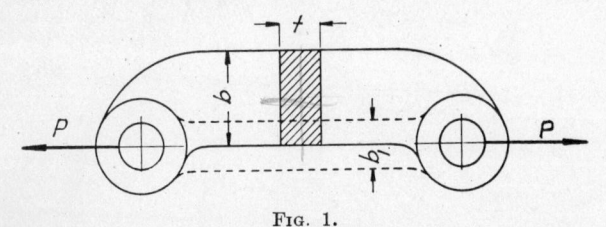

FIG. 1.

inch and that $b_1 = 2.5\ t$. (*b*) Due to certain changes made in the design of the machine, it was necessary to replace the original link by an unsymmetrical one, shown by the full

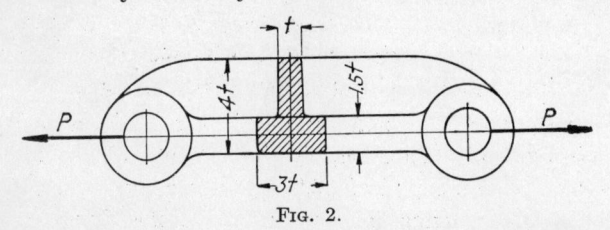

FIG. 2.

lines, having the same thickness t as the original link. Using the same permissible stress as before, determine the depth b.

2.—The statement of this problem is identical with that of Prob. 1, with the exception that the force P is 28,200 lb.

3.—The statement of this problem is identical with that of Prob. 1, with the exception that the force P is 38,000 lb.

4.—It is required to determine the dimensions of the principal cross-section of the cast iron unsymmetrical link shown in Fig. 2,

2 PROBLEMS IN MACHINE DESIGN

having given the magnitude of the force P as 7,600 lb. and the dimensions of the cross-section as shown in the figure. Assume the permissible tensile and compressive stresses of the material are 3,000 and 12,000 lb. per square inch respectively.

5.—The statement of this problem is identical with that of Prob. 4, with the exception that the force P is 13,500 lb.

6.—The statement of this problem is identical with that of Prob. 4, with the exception that the force P is 16,000 lb.

7.—The body of the cast iron unsymmetrical link shown in Fig. 2 has the proportions given in Fig. 3(a). Determine the load P that this link may safely carry, so that the permissible tensile

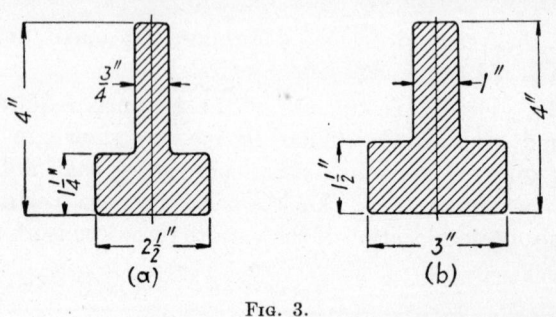

FIG. 3.

and compressive stresses in the principal section shall not exceed 2,500 and 10,000 lb. per square inch respectively.

8.—The statement of this problem is identical with that of Prob. 7, with the exception that the principal cross-section of the body of the link has the proportions given in Fig. 3(b).

9.—In the boom of a pillar crane, the central force acting down through the boom has a magnitude of 40,000 lb.; in addition to this force there is a pull of 12,000 lb. on a rope, the center line of which is 9 in. from the center line of the channels forming the boom. Determine the economical size of the channels, having given the following data: Unbraced length of the boom is 11 ft. 6 in.; modulus of elasticity is 30,000.000; stress at the elastic limit is 30,000; permissible working stress is 10,000 to 12,000 lb. per square inch; the coefficient n is 1.

10 to 13.—The main frame of a rope-geared air cylinder consists of two steel channels bolted to the cylinder, as shown in Fig. 4. The lines of action of the forces on the frame, due to the air pressure and rope loads, are clearly shown in the figure and data, pertaining to the magnitude and location of the forces and the size of the channels, are contained in Table 1. Disregarding the stresses due to the load Q and the weights of the

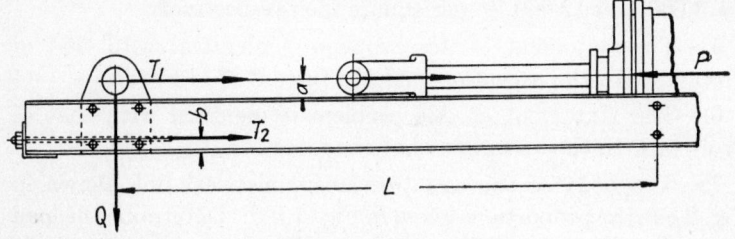

FIG. 4.

cylinder, sheaves and frame, determine the maximum stress produced in the frame channels.

13 to 17.—Determine the size of the channels required for a rope-geared air cylinder similar to the one shown in Fig. 4, assuming that the maximum permissible stress shall not exceed 10,000 lb. per square inch. For the necessary data, pertaining to the magnitude and location of the various forces, consult Table 1.

TABLE 1

Problem number	P	Q	T_1	T_2	a	b	L	Size of channels
10	1,690	740	810	880	1	1¼	74	3 by 4.1 lb.
11	3,380	1,500	1,625	1,755	1¼	1½	77	4 by 5.4 lb.
12	10,300	4,680	4,990	5,310	2⅛	2	86	6 by 8.2 lb.
13	5,680	2,540	2,735	2,945	1½	1½	81	
14	14,100	6,510	6,860	7,240	2¾	2½	90	
15	21,300	9,960	10,410	10,890	3⅛	2½	94	
16	26,900	12,560	13,120	13,780	3¼	2½	94	

17 to 22.—(a) For a drop-forged clamp, similar in design to that shown in Fig. 5 and having the dimensions given in Table 2, determine the compressive stress produced in the screw, assuming the section of the clamp body along AB may be subjected to a maximum tensile or compressive stress of 22,000 and 18,000 lb. per square inch respectively. (b) Using the load P upon the screw as found above, determine the magnitude of the resultant stresses in the section along CD.

TABLE 2

Problem number	a	Section AB		Section CD		r	Screw	
		b	c	b	c		Diameter	Length
17	1 11/16	1 3/16	9/16	1 7/16	9/16	5/8	9/16	3 1/4
18	2 1/2	2 1/8	11/16	1 15/16	11/16	3/4	3/4	4 3/8
19	2 7/8	2 1/4	11/16	2 1/8	11/16	3/4	7/8	5
20	3	2 7/8	3/4	2 5/8	3/4	1/2	1	7
21	3 3/16	2 7/8	3/4	2 5/8	3/4	5/8	1	7 1/2

22.—Assuming that the maximum permissible compression in the screw of the drop-forged clamp, shown in Fig. 5, is 12,000

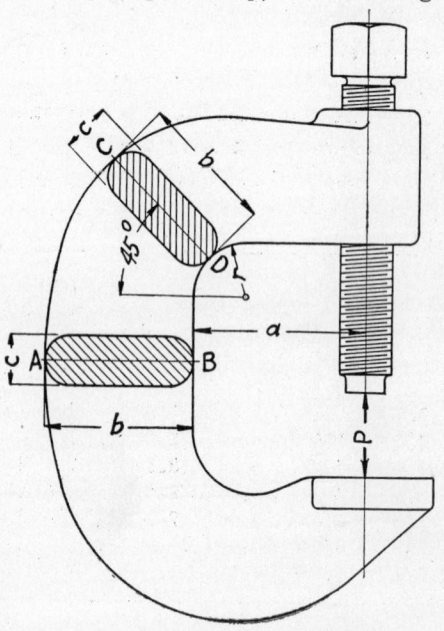

FIG. 5.

lb. per square inch, determine the intensity of the resultant stresses produced in the sections along AB and CD respectively, using the proportions given in Prob. 17.

23.—The statement of this problem is identical with that of Prob. 22, with the exception that the proportions given in Prob. 18 be used.

STRESSES AND STRAINS IN MACHINE PARTS 5

24.—The statement of this problem is identical with that of Prob. 22, with the exception that the proportions given in Prob. 19 be used.

25.—The statement of this problem is identical with that of Prob. 22, with the exception that the proportions given in Prob. 20 be used.

26.—The statement of this problem is identical with that of Prob. 22, with the exception that the proportions given in Prob. 21 be used.

27 to 30.—(a) For a drop-forged clamp, similar in design to that shown in Fig. 6 and having the dimensions given in Table 3, determine the compressive stress produced in the screw, assuming the section of the clamp body along AB may be subjected to a maximum tensile or compressive stress of 20,000 and 17,000 lb. per square inch respectively. (b) Using the load P upon the screw as calculated above, determine the magnitude of the resultant stresses in the section along CD.

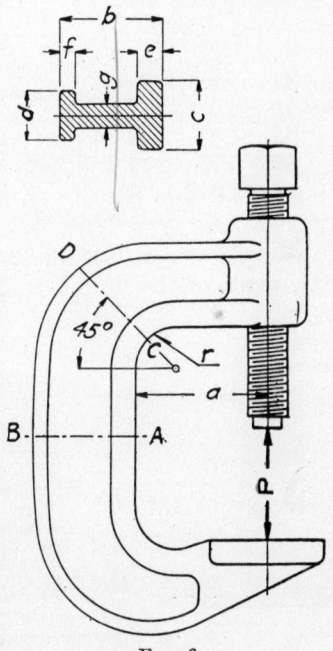

Fig. 6.

TABLE 3

Problem number	a	Section AB						Section CD					r	Screw	
		b	c	d	e	f	g	b	c	d	e	f	g		Diameter	Length
27	1 9/16	1 1/4	3/4	1/2	5/16	3/16	1/4	1 1/8	Same as for Section AB					5/16	7/16	2 3/4
28	2 7/8	2 1/4	1 1/16	1	9/16	5/16	1/2	2 1/8						7/8	7/8	5
29	3 1/2	3 3/8	1 11/16	1 3/16	3/4	1/2	1/2	2 5/8						7/8	1 1/8	8 1/2

30.—Assuming that the maximum permissible compression in the screw of the drop-forged clamp, shown in Fig. 6, is 12,000 lb. per square inch, what is the magnitude of the resultant stresses produced in the sections along AB and CD respectively, using the proportions given in Prob. 27?

31.—The statement of this problem is identical with that of Prob. 30, with the exception that the proportions given in Prob. 28 be used.

32.—The statement of this problem is identical with that of Prob. 30, with the exception that the proportions given in Prob. 29 be used.

33 to 38.—In Fig. 7 is shown a boat davit proportioned according to the data given in Table 4. (a) Determine the maximum resultant stresses produced in the material of a section at right angles to the line of action of the load P. (b) What are the unit pressures coming upon the bearings A and B? (c) What tensile stress is produced in the journal C?

38 to 43.—A boat davit, similar in design to that shown in Fig. 7, is built according to the dimensions given in Table 4. (a) What is the maximum load P that may be suspended from the davit, assuming the resultant fiber stress in the material shall not exceed the stress S given in the table? (b) Due to the load P, what are the unit pressures coming upon the bearings A and B? (c) What is the tensile stress produced in the journal C?

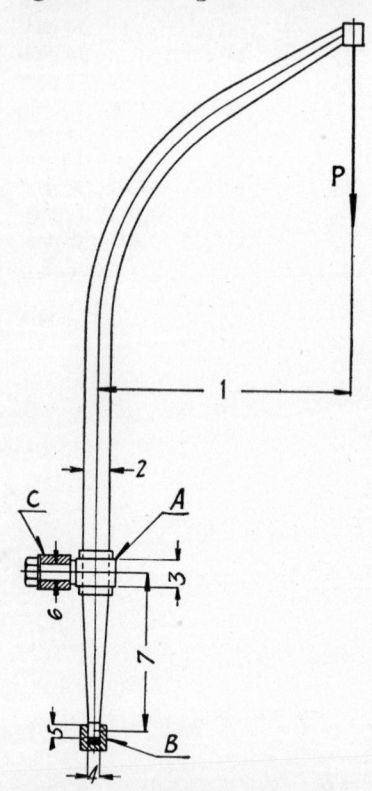

Fig. 7.

43 to 49.—For a boat davit, similar in design to the one shown in Fig. 7, determine the diameter of the mast, namely, the dimension (2), using the data given in Table 4. (NOTE.—For diameters above 6 in., work to the nearest ½ in. and below 6 in., use ¼ in. increments.)

TABLE 4

Problem number	Dimensions							Load P	Permissible stress S
	1	2	3	4	5	6	7		
33	61	3½	3⅞	2½	2½	2¼	31¼	800	
34	60	5	5⅜	2½	2½	3	40¼	2,900	
35	109	7½	7⅞	3	2½	5	43¼	5,370	
36	105	9	9⅜	4	2½	6	49¼	9,530	
37	97	10	10⅜	4	2½	6½	52¼	15,070	
38	56	4	4⅜	2½	2½	2½	34¼	......	14,000
39	82	6	6⅜	3	2½	3½	40¼	......	13,000
40	76	7	7⅜	3	2½	4½	43¼	......	15,000
41	88	8½	8⅞	4	2½	5½	49¼	......	14,000
42	108	10	10⅜	4	2½	6½	52¼	......	15,000
43	99	....	....	...	...	...	52¼	12,430	12,500
44	96	....	....	...	...	...	49¼	10,740	14,000
45	87	....	....	...	...	...	52¼	6,430	15,000
46	74	....	....	...	...	...	43¼	4,580	15,000
47	66	....	....	...	...	...	40¼	2,400	14,000
48	84	....	....	...	...	...	34¼	1,550	15,000

SECTION II

RIVETED CONNECTIONS

49 to **53.**—The girth seam of a horizontal tubular boiler, designed according to the A. S. M. E. specifications, is of the single-riveted lap-joint type. The joint is proportioned according to the data given in Table 5 and the allowable working stresses in tension, shearing and bearing are 11,000, 8,800 and 19,000 lb. per square inch respectively. Determine the efficiency of the joint and the manner in which it will fail.

53 to **57.**—The longitudinal seam of a pressure tank, designed according to the A. S. M. E. specifications, is of the double-riveted lap-joint type. The joint is proportioned according to the data given in Table 5 and the permissible tensile, shearing and bearing stresses shall not exceed 11,000, 8,800 and 19,000 lb. per square inch respectively. Determine the efficiency of the joint and the manner in which it will fail.

TABLE 5

Problem number	Type of joint	Thickness of shell	Nominal rivet diameter	Pitch	Back-pitch	Margin
49	Single-riveted lap	1/4	5/8	1 3/4	...	1 1/16
50		5/16	3/4	1 7/8	...	1 1/4
51		3/8	3/4	1 7/8	...	1 7/16
52		1/2	7/8	2 1/8	...	1 5/8
53	Double-riveted lap	1/4	5/8	2 1/4	1 3/4	1 1/16
54		5/16	3/4	2 5/8	1 7/8	1 1/4
55		3/8	7/8	3	2	1 7/16
56		1/2	1	3 3/8	2 1/8	1 5/8

57 to **69.**—The longitudinal seam of a pressure tank, designed according to the A. S. M. E. specifications, is of the butt-joint type. The joint is proportioned according to the data given in Table 6 and the permissible tensile, shearing and bearing stresses shall not exceed 11,000, 8,800 and 19,000 lb. per square inch. Determine the efficiency of the joint and the manner in which it will fail.

TABLE 6

Problem number	Type of joint	Thickness of shell	Thickness of strap plates	Nominal rivet diameter	Long pitch	Back-pitch Inner	Back-pitch Middle	Back-pitch Outer	Margin
57	Double-	1/4	1/4	5/8	4	2 1/8	....	....	1 1/16
58	riveted	5/16	9/32	3/4	4 1/2	2 7/16	....	....	1 1/4
59	butt	3/8	5/16	3/4	4 1/2	2 7/16	....	....	1 1/4
60		1/2	7/16	7/8	5	2 3/4	....	....	1 7/16
61	Triple-	3/8	5/16	3/4	7	1 7/8	....	2 7/16	1 1/4
62	riveted	1/2	7/16	7/8	8	2	....	2 3/4	1 5/16
63	butt	5/8	1/2	1	8	2 1/4	....	3	1 5/8
64		3/4	1/2	1 1/8	8 1/4	2 3/8	....	3 1/4	1 13/16
65		3/8	5/16	3/4	14	1 7/8	2 7/16	2 3/4	1 1/4
66	Quad.-	1/2	7/16	7/8	16	2	2 3/4	3 1/8	1 7/16
67	riveted	5/8	1/2	1	16	2 1/4	3	3 5/16	1 5/8
68	butt	3/4	1/2	1 1/8	16 1/2	2 3/8	3 1/4	3 9/16	1 13/16

69 to 72.—In an air receiver, designed to fulfill the requirements of the A. S. M. E. Boiler Code, a double-riveted lap-joint is used for the longitudinal seam. If the shell and joint are made according to the dimensions given in Table 7, what pressure may be safely carried in the receiver so that the allowable tensile, shearing and bearing stresses shall not exceed 11,000, 8,800 and 19,000 lb. per square inch respectively? What is the efficiency of the joint?

TABLE 7

Problem number	Type of joint	Shell diameter	Thickness of shell	Thickness of strap plates	Nominal rivet diameter	Long pitch	Back-pitch Inner	Back-pitch Outer	Margin
69	Double-	36	3/8	...	7/8	3	2	...	1 1/16
70	riveted	48	1/2	...	1	3 3/8	2 1/8	...	1 5/8
71	lap	60	7/16	...	1	3 3/8	2 1/8	...	1 5/8
72	Double-	60	3/8	5/16	3/4	4 1/2	2 7/16	...	1 1/4
73	riveted	66	7/16	3/8	7/8	5	2 3/4	...	1 7/16
74	butt	72	1/2	7/16	7/8	5	2 3/4	...	1 7/16
75	Triple-	66	1/2	7/16	7/8	8	2	2 3/4	1 7/16
76	riveted	72	5/8	1/2	1	8	2 1/4	3	1 5/8
77	butt	84	3/4	1/2	1 1/8	8 1/4	2 3/8	3 1/4	1 13/16

72 to 78.—The longitudinal seam of a steam boiler, designed to fulfill the requirements of the A. S. M. E. Boiler Code, is of the butt-joint type. If the shell and joint are made according to the dimensions given in Table 7, determine the efficiency of the joint and the pressure that may be safely carried in the boiler, assuming that the allowable tensile, shearing and bearing stresses are not to exceed 11,000, 8,800 and 19,000 lb. per square inch respectively.

78.—It is required to design a double-riveted lap-joint for the longitudinal seam of a pressure tank, 38 in. in diameter, subjected to an internal pressure of 125 lb. per square inch. The proportions of the joint must fulfill the requirements of the A. S. M. E. Boiler Code. Assume that the permissible tensile, shearing and bearing stresses are not to exceed 11,000, 8,800 and 19,000 lb. per square inch respectively.

79.—The statement of this problem is identical with that of Prob. 78, with the exception that the diameter of the tank is 48 in. and the pressure is 150 lb. per square inch.

80.—The statement of this problem is identical with that of Prob. 78, with the exception that the diameter of the tank is 42 in. and the pressure is 175 lb. per square inch.

81.—Design a double-riveted butt-joint for the longitudinal seam of a steam drum, 36 in. in diameter, subjected to an internal pressure of 250 lb. per square inch. The proportions of the joint must fulfill the requirements of the A. S. M. E. Boiler Code. The permissible tensile, shearing and bearing stresses may be assumed as 11,000, 8,800 and 19,000 lb. per square inch respectively.

82.—The statement of this problem is identical with that of Prob. 81, with the exception that the diameter of the drum is 42 in. and the pressure is 200 lb. per square inch.

83.—The statement of this problem is identical with that of Prob. 81, with the exception that the diameter of the drum is 48 in. and the pressure is 175 lb. per square inch.

84.—The statement of this problem is identical with that of Prob. 81, with the exception that the diameter of the drum is 54 in. and the pressure is 165 lb. per square inch.

85.—Design a triple-riveted butt-joint for the longitudinal seam of a steam-boiler shell 60 in. in diameter, subjected to an internal pressure of 175 lb. per square inch. The proportions of the joint must fulfill the requirements of the A. S. M. E. Boiler Code. Use the same stresses as given in Prob. 78.

86.—The statement of this problem is identical with that of Prob. 85, with the exception that the diameter of the shell is 66 in.

87.—The statement of this problem is identical with that of Prob. 85, with the exception that the diameter of the shell is 72 in. and the pressure is 150 lb. per square inch.

88.—The statement of this problem is identical with that of Prob. 85, with the exception that the diameter of the shell is 72 in. and the pressure is 175 lb. per square inch.

89.—The jib or boom, supporting the head sheave of a crane, consists of two 10-in. by 15-lb. channels arranged as shown in

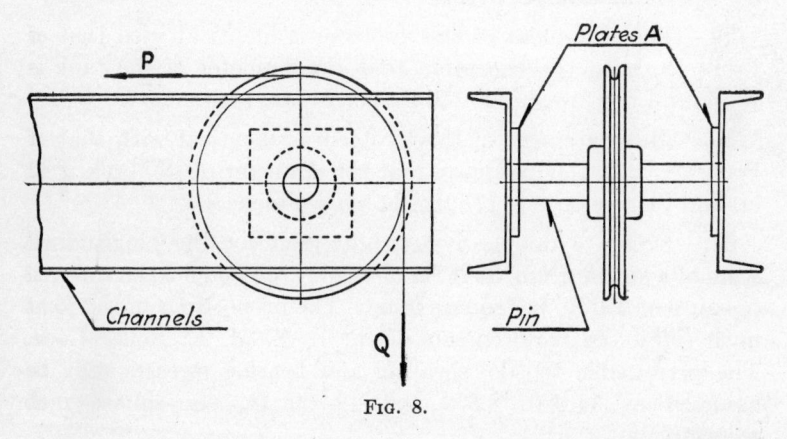

FIG. 8.

Fig. 8. Determine the thickness of the reënforcing plates A and the number of ¾-in. rivets required for supporting the sheave pin, having given the following data: Loads P and Q are 14,000 lb. each; diameter of the sheave pin is 2 in.; the permissible shearing and bearing stresses for the materials used in the construction are 6,000 and 10,000 lb. per square inch respectively.

90.—The boom, supporting the two 21-in. head sheaves of a locomotive crane, consists of two 12-in. by 25-lb. channels arranged as shown in Fig. 8. Determine the thickness of the reënforcing plates and the number of ¾-in. rivets required for supporting the 2½-in. sheave pin having given the following data: Loads P and Q are 16,000 lb. each; the permissible shearing and bearing stresses for the materials, used in the construction, are 6,000 and 10,000 lb. per square inch respectively.

91.—(a) Determine the resultant shearing stress coming upon each of the ¾-in. rivets used in the riveted connection shown in Fig. 9, assuming the force P has a magnitude of 8,400 lb. (b) Assuming 16,000 lb. per square inch as the permissible tensile stress, determine the economical size of the angle A.

92.—Determine the economical size of the angle A and the number of ¾-in. rivets required in each member of a riveted connection, similar to the one shown in Fig. 9, having given the

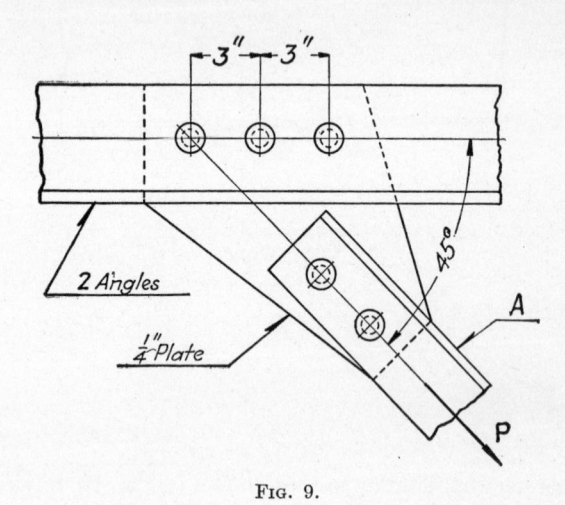

FIG. 9.

following data: Magnitude of P is 9,500 lb.; thickness of the gusset plate is ⅜ in.; pitch of the rivets in the horizontal member is 3 in.; the permissible stresses in tension, shearing and bearing are 16,000, 10,000 and 20,000 lb. per square inch respectively.

93.—In a riveted connection, similar to that shown in Fig. 9, the member A consists of two 3 by 2½ by ¼-in. angles fastened to the horizontal angles by a ⅜-in. gusset plate. Five ¾-in. rivets, spaced 3 in. apart, are used in the upper group of rivets and four in the lower. Assuming that the line of action of the load P passes through the end rivet of the upper group, what load may safely be carried by this connection so that allowable tensile, shearing and bearing stresses shall not exceed 16,000, 10,000 and 20,000 lb. per square inch respectively?

94.—What load P may safely be carried by the riveted connection shown in Fig. 10, if the unbraced length of the strut A is 110 in. and that all rivets are ¾ in. in diameter? Assume the tensile, compressive, shearing and bearing stresses are not to exceed 12,000, 10,000, 7,500 and 15,000 lb. per square inch respectively.

95.—Determine the economical size of the angle in the strut A and the number of ¾-in. rivets required in each member of a

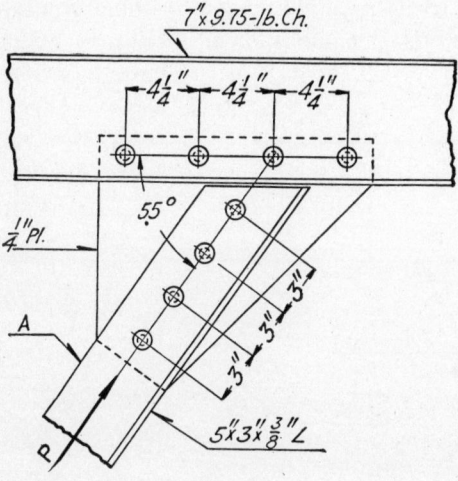

FIG. 10.

riveted connection, similar to that shown in Fig. 10, having given the following data: Magnitude of P is 11,300 lb.; pitch of the rivets in the channel is 4 in.; the thickness of the gusset plate and the size of channel are as shown in Fig. 10; the permissible tensile, shearing, bearing and compressive stresses are 12,000, 7,500, 15,000 and 10,000 lb. per square inch respectively; the unbraced length of the strut A is 102 in

96.—Determine the economical size of the angle in the member A and the number of ¾-in. rivets required in each member of a riveted connection, similar to that shown in Fig. 10, assuming the force P is reversed in direction and having given the following data: Magnitude of P is 14,500 lb.; thickness of the gusset plate is ⅜ in.; size of channel 9 in. by 13.25 lb.; pitch of the rivets in the channel is 4 in.; the allowable tensile, shearing and bearing stresses are not to exceed 16,000, 10,000 and 20,000 lb. per square inch respectively.

97.—What load P may safely be carried by the riveted connection shown in Fig. 11, if the unbraced length of the strut A is 110 in. and that ¾-in. rivets are used? The allowable tensile, compressive, shearing and bearing stresses are not to exceed 12,000, 10,000, 7,500 and 15,000 lb. per square inch respectively.

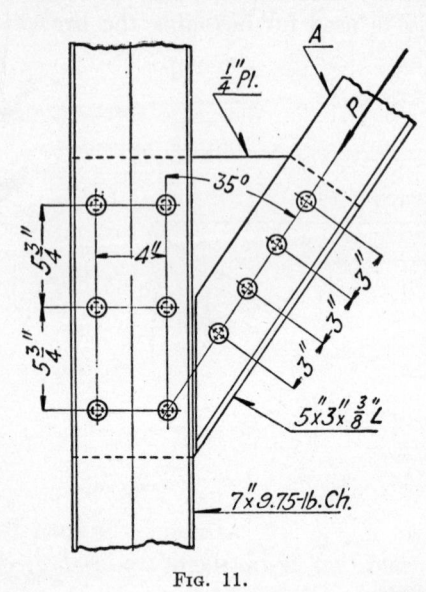

98.—If the direction of the force P in Fig. 11 is reversed, what force may safely be carried by the connection, assuming ¾-in. rivets are used and that the permissible tensile, shearing and bearing stresses are not to exceed 12,000, 7,500 and 15,000 lb. per square inch respectively?

Fig. 11.

99.—For the riveted connection, shown in Fig. 12, determine the resultant shearing and bearing stresses coming upon each rivet used for fastening the bracket to the column channel. Assume the magnitude of the load P as 4,000 lb. and the diameter of the rivets as ¾ in.

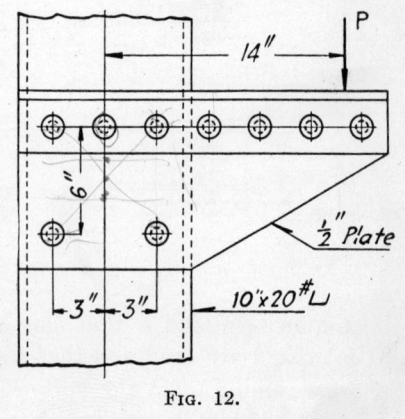

100.—Determine the maximum safe load P that may be supported by the bracket shown in Fig. 12, assuming the rivets are ¾ in. in diameter and that the shearing and bearing stresses, coming upon the rivets, shall not exceed 10,000 and 20,000 lb. per square inch respectively.

Fig. 12.

101.—What load P may safely be carried by the bracket shown in Fig. 13, assuming the rivets are ¾ in. in diameter and that the shearing and bearing stresses, coming upon the rivets, shall not exceed 10,000 and 20,000 lb. per square inch respectively?

102.—Determine the resultant shearing and bearing stresses coming upon each of the rivets used for fastening the bracket

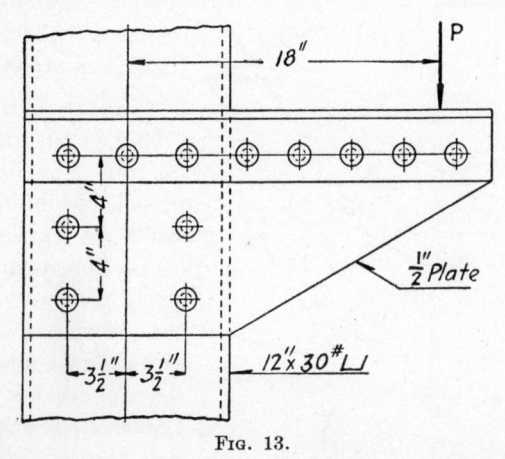

FIG. 13.

to the column channel shown in Fig. 13. Assume the load P has a magnitude of 5,000 lb. and that $\frac{3}{4}$-in. rivets are used.

103.—In Fig. 14 is shown a form of built-up structural steel bracket used for supporting a guide sheave. Determine the

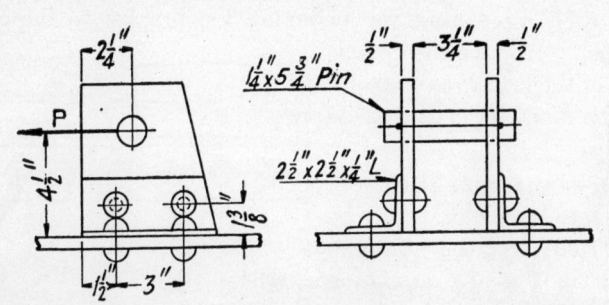

FIG. 14.

maximum safe load P that this bracket will support, assuming $\frac{5}{8}$-in. rivets are used and that the tensile, shearing and bearing stresses coming upon the various parts shall not exceed 12,000, 7,500 and 15,000 lb. per square inch respectively.

104.—In the riveted connection, shown in Fig. 15, the compression in the top chord A is 52,100 lb. and the tension in the lower chord B is 47,800 lb. The vertical and horizontal components of the reaction coming upon the member C are 22,500 lb. and 3,400 lb. respectively. Determine the following: (a) The economical size of the angles used for the top chord, assuming the

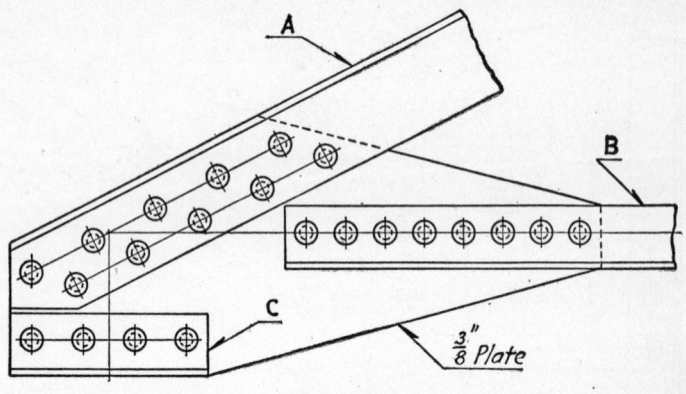

Fig. 15.

unbraced length of the member as 8 ft. 9 in. (b) The economical size of the angles used for the lower chord assuming a working stress of 16,000 lb. per square inch. (c) The bearing and shearing stresses coming upon the rivets in the various members, assuming $\frac{3}{4}$-in. rivets are used and that the angles C are of the same size as those used in the lower chord B.

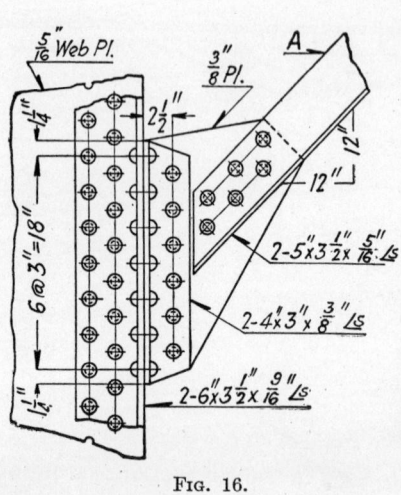

Fig. 16.

105.—Determine the maximum tensile load that the member A of the riveted connection, shown in Fig. 16, will safely carry, assuming that all rivets are $\frac{3}{4}$ in. in diameter and that the tensile, shearing and bearing stresses shall not exceed 16,000, 10,000 and 20,000 lb. per square inch respectively.

106.—For the riveted connection, shown in Fig. 17, determine the following: (a) If the member A is built up of two $3\frac{1}{2}$ by $2\frac{1}{2}$ by $\frac{5}{16}$-in. angles and the unbraced length is 10 ft. 4 in.,

RIVETED CONNECTIONS 17

what load P will it safely carry assuming an allowable compressive stress of 14,000 lb. per square inch? (b) Using the load P found above, determine the resultant shearing and bearing stresses

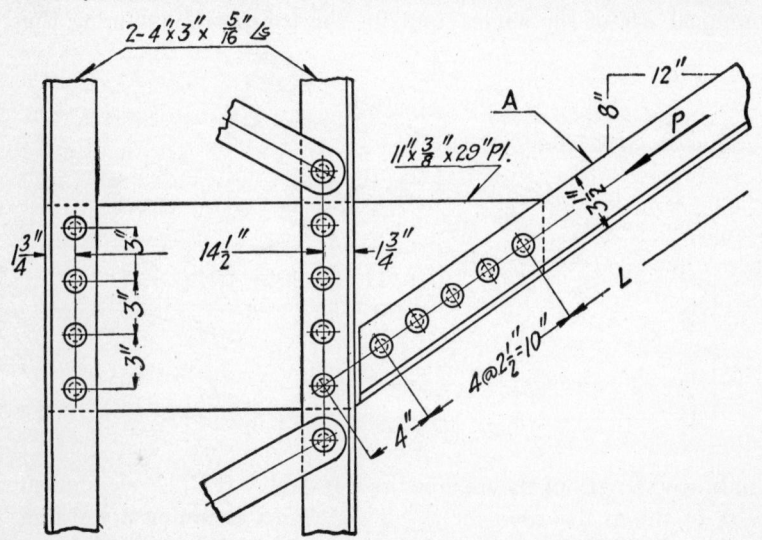

FIG. 17.

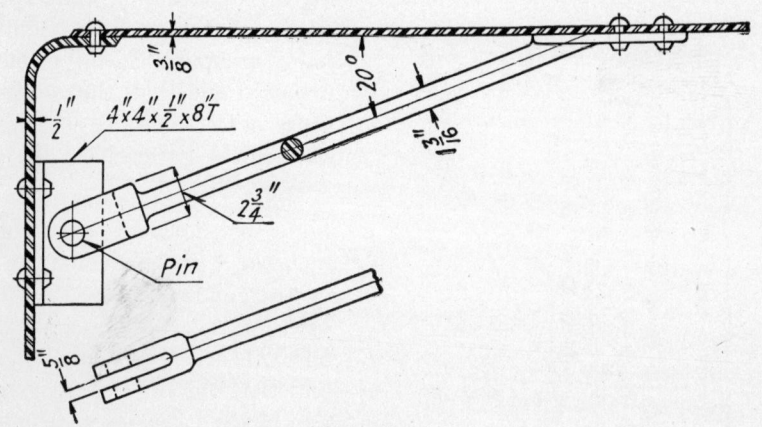

FIG. 18.

coming upon the various rivets used in the connection, assuming $\frac{3}{4}$-in. rivets are used.

107.—The boiler brace, shown in Fig. 18, supports an area of 80 sq. in. on the boiler head. Determine the various dimensions of the brace and pin, also the number of $\frac{3}{4}$-in. rivets required to fasten the brace and T-bar, having given the following data: (a) The steam pressure in the boiler is 120 lb. per square inch. (b) The shearing and bearing stresses for the rivets may be taken as 7,500 and 15,000 lb. per square inch respectively. (c) The tensile, shearing and bearing stresses for the pin may be taken as 12,000, 7,500 and 15,000 lb. per square inch respectively.

Crowfoot Stays.—In Fig. 19 is shown a crowfoot stay, also called diagonal boiler brace, which is used for connecting the unsupported area of the head to the shell of a boiler. In design-

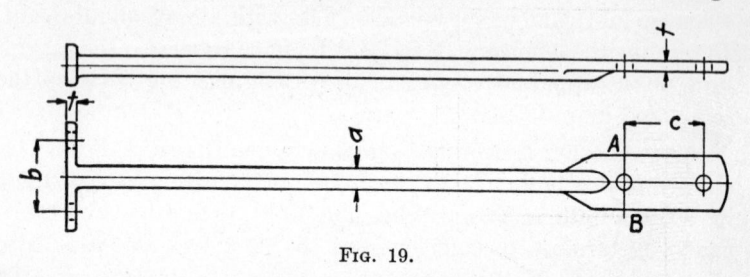

FIG. 19.

ing a stay of this kind, the following requirements must be fulfilled: (a) The two rivets at each end of the stay must have a combined cross-sectional area equivalent to at least one and one-quarter times the area of the body of the stay. (b) The net cross-sectional area through the center of each rivet hole in the blade, as at AB, must be at least one and one-quarter times the area of the body of the stay. (c) The net area through the center of each rivet hole in the crowfoot, must be at least one-half of the net area through a rivet hole in the blade. (d) Each branch of the crowfoot must be capable of carrying two-thirds of the total load coming upon the body.

108.—Having given the following data, determine all of the missing dimensions of a crowfoot stay, assuming the maximum permissible tensile stress in the body as 8,500 lb. per square inch: (a) Diameter a of the body is $1\frac{1}{8}$ in.; thickness $t = \frac{1}{2}$ in.; distances b and c are $4\frac{1}{4}$ in. and 5 in. respectively.

109.—The statement of this problem is identical with that of Prob. 108, with the exception that the diameter a is $1\frac{3}{16}$ in. and the thickness t is $\frac{9}{16}$ in.

110.—The statement of this problem is identical with that of Prob. 108, with the exception that the diameter a is $1\frac{1}{4}$ in. and the thickness t is $\frac{5}{8}$ in.

SECTION III

BOLTS AND SCREWS

111.—By an actual test on a screw jack, having a screw $1\frac{1}{2}$ in. in diameter and $\frac{1}{3}$-in. pitch, it was found that a pull of 90 lb. at the end of a 12-in. lever was required to raise a load of 2,360 lb. when no lubricant was used, and 79 lb. with a hard oil lubricant. Determine the efficiency of the jack for each case, also the magnitude of the apparent coefficient of friction existing between the screw and its nut.

112.—Another test on the screw jack mentioned in Prob. 111, showed that a pull of 50 lb. was required to raise a load of 1,205 lb. when no lubricant was used, and 40 lb. with a hard oil lubricant. Determine the efficiency of the jack for each case, also the magnitude of the apparent coefficient of friction existing between the screw and its nut.

113.—Determine the magnitude of the effort required at the end of a 10-in. wrench to cause failure of a $\frac{1}{2}$-in. U. S. Std. bolt by tension, assuming no lubrication of the thread ($\mu' = 0.30$) and that the ultimate tensile strength of the bolt material is 60,000 lb. per square inch.

114.—The statement of this problem is identical with that of Prob. 113, with the exception that the length of the wrench and the diameter of the bolt are 16 in. and $\frac{3}{4}$ in. respectively.

115.—Determine the magnitude of the effort required at the end of an 18-in. wrench to cause failure of a $1\frac{1}{2}$-in. U. S. Std. bolt by tension, assuming no lubrication of the thread ($\mu' = 0.30$) and that the ultimate tensile strength of the bolt material is 80,000 lb. per square inch.

116.—Determine the maximum effort that can be exerted at the end of a 16-in. wrench in order that the maximum tensile stress in a 1-in. U. S. Std. bolt shall not exceed 10,000 lb. per square inch, assuming no lubrication of the thread ($\mu' = 0.30$).

117.—The statement of this problem is identical with that of Prob. 116, with the exception that the length of the wrench and the diameter of the bolt are 14 in. and $\frac{3}{4}$ in. respectively.

118.—The statement of this problem is identical with that of Prob. 116, with the exception that the length of the wrench and the diameter of the bolt are 12 in. and ⅝ in. respectively.

119.—A screw jack, having a screw 1½ in. in diameter and ⅓-in. pitch, has nine threads in contact with the nut. Assume the coefficient of friction between the screw and the nut to be 0.25. (*a*) Determine the lifting capacity of the screw jack if the unit bearing pressure on the thread is to be kept within safe limits.

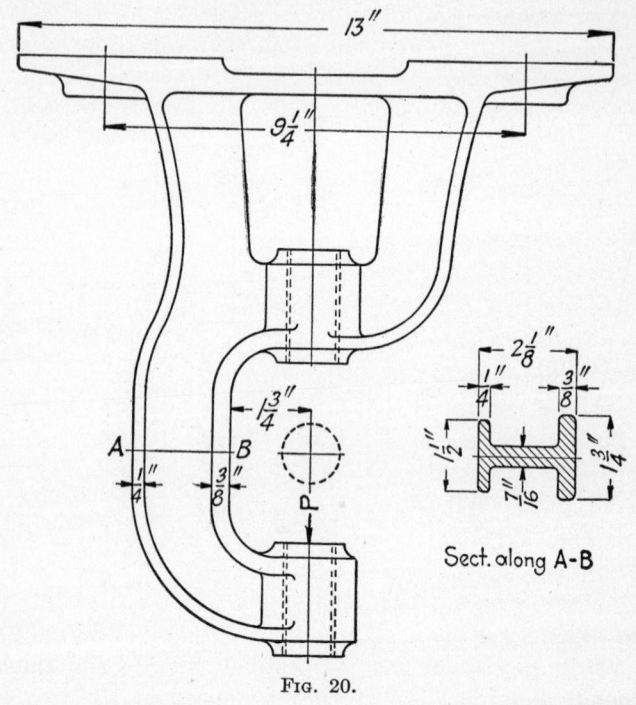

Fig. 20.

(*b*) What effort must be exerted at the end of a 12-in. lever in order to raise this load? (*c*) What load can be raised with a pull of 50 lb. on the 12-in. lever?

120.—For the shaft hanger, shown in Fig. 20, determine the magnitude of the load P, assuming that the permissible tensile and compressive stresses in the section AB shall not exceed 1,500 and 3,500 lb. per square inch. If the hanger is fastened by means of two ¾-in. bolts, what stress is produced in the bolts?

121.—For the crane-runway bracket, shown in Fig. 21, determine the following, having given the magnitude of the load

P as 3,000 lb.: (a) The maximum tensile and compressive stresses produced in the section along AB. (b) The stresses produced in the two 1-in. bolts used in fastening the bracket to the roof truss.

122.—(a) What load is the crane-runway bracket, shown in Fig. 21, capable of supporting so that the tensile and compressive

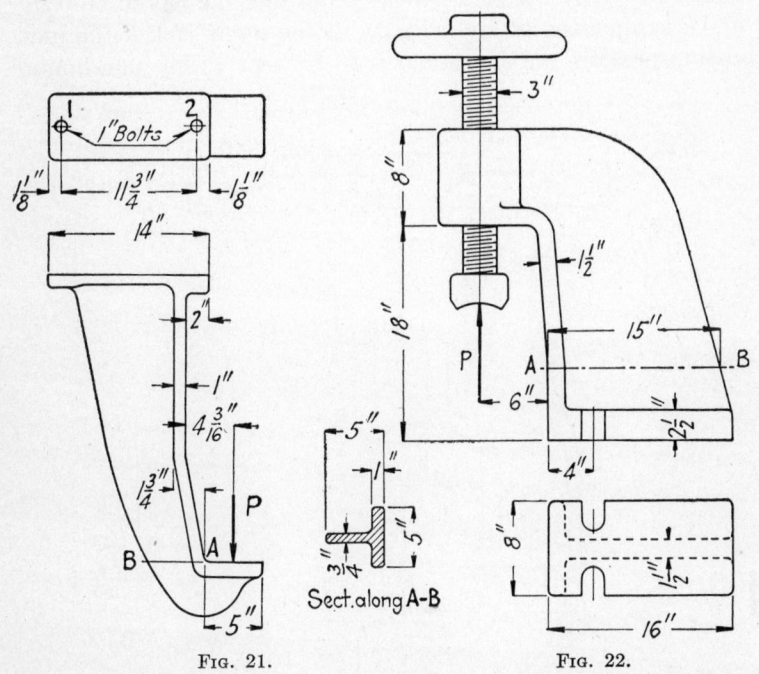

FIG. 21.

FIG. 22.

stresses produced in the section along AB shall not exceed 2,500 and 3,500 lb. per square inch respectively? (b) Using the load just found, determine the stresses produced in the two 1-in. bolts used in fastening the bracket to the roof truss.

123.—(a) It is required to determine the pressure P that the screw of the bracket clamp shown in Fig. 22 can exert, so that the compressive stress in the screw shall not exceed 10,000 lb. per square inch. Assume the screw has four square threads per inch. (b) Determine the bearing pressure coming upon the threads, also the efficiency of the screw, assuming $\mu' = 0.1$. (c) Determine the maximum stresses produced in the section AB, when the load upon the screw has the magnitude determined in (a). (d) Determine the size of the two bolts used to fasten the bracket clamp to the platen, assuming the permissible tensile stress is 20,000 lb. per square inch.

124.—(a) Determine the maximum tensile and compressive stresses in the sections along AB and CD of the bond compressor shown in Fig. 23, assuming the load P has a magnitude of 12,000 lb. (b) Determine the compressive stress and the bearing pres-

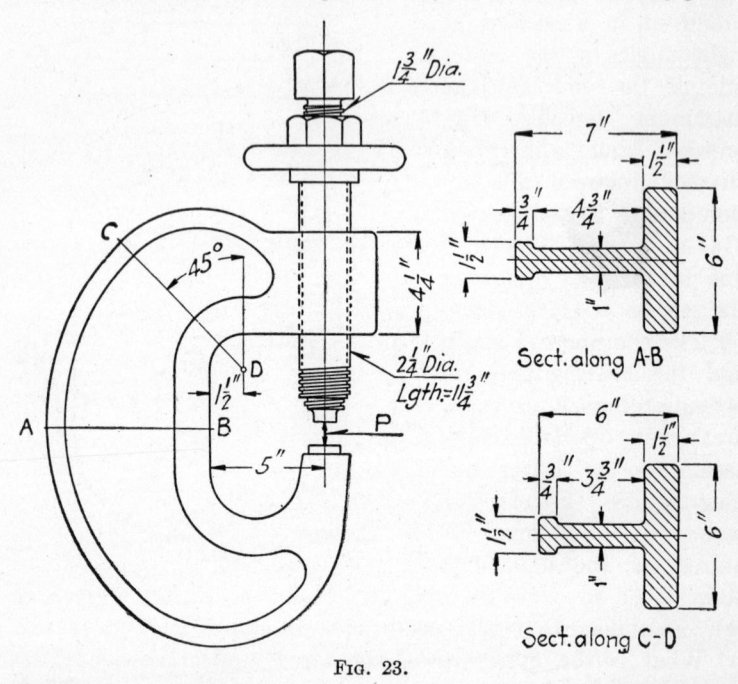

Fig. 23.

sure per square inch of projected area coming upon each screw, having given the pitch of each of the screws as $\frac{1}{4}$ in. (c) What force is required at the end of a 24-in. wrench, in order that the operating screw will produce the force P given in (a), assuming that the coefficient of screw friction is 0.2? (d) What is the efficiency of the operating screw under the conditions stated in (c)?

125.—(a) In the bond compressor shown in Fig. 23, a force of 120 lb. is applied at the end of a 24-in. wrench, what axial pressure is produced by the operating screw assuming that the coefficient of screw friction is 0.2? (b) What is the efficiency of the operating screw under the conditions stated in (a)? (c) Determine the compressive stress and the bearing pressure per square inch of projected area coming upon each screw, assuming the pitch in each case to be ¼ in. (d) Using the force P found in (a), determine the maximum tensile and compressive stresses in the sections along AB and CD.

126.—Having given the capacity of the hand punch, shown in Fig. 24, as a $1\tfrac{3}{16}$-in. hole in a ⅜-in. steel plate, determine the following: (a) The maximum tensile and compressive stresses produced in a section at right angles to the center line of the die. (b) The maximum tensile, compressive and shearing stresses produced in a section parallel to and located 3½ in. back of the center line of the die, assuming the section is 4⅝ in. deep. (c) The compressive stress and the bearing pressure per square inch of projected area coming upon the screw, assuming the latter has four square threads per inch. (d) The force required at the end of a 30-in. lever so as to be able to obtain the capacity given in (a), assuming that the coefficient of screw friction is 0.2. (e) What is the efficiency of the screw under the conditions stated in (d)?

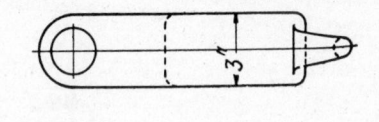

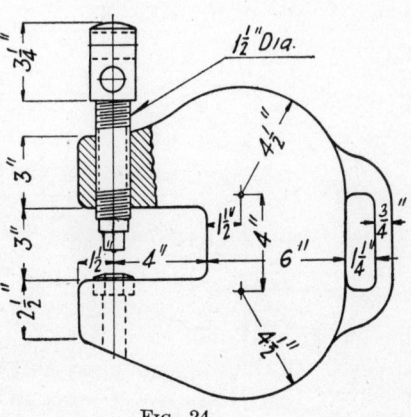

Fig. 24.

127.—A bearing, similar to the one shown in Fig. 36 of the author's text on "Machine Design" is fastened to the frame of a machine by means of four ¾-in. cap screws spaced equally on a 9-in. bolt circle. The bearing flange is 12 in. in diameter and the load of 5,600 lb. is located 4 in. from the frame. (a) Establish a formula for the maximum load coming upon any screw. (b) Determine the maximum tensile and shearing stresses coming upon any cap screw. (c) Assuming that the cap screws are relieved from all shearing action by the use of two ⅝-in. dowel pins, determine the magnitude of the shearing stress in these pins.

128.—A flanged bearing, having the same dimensions as the bearing described in Prob. 127, supports a load of 4,800 lb. at a distance of 4½ in. from the frame. (*a*) Establish a formula for the maximum load coming upon any screw. (*b*) Determine the size of the cap screws required for this bearing, assuming the maximum permissible tensile and shearing stresses shall not exceed 8,000 and 6,000 lb. per square inch respectively. (*c*) Determine the size of the dowel pins required to relieve the cap screws from all shearing action, assuming an allowable shearing stress of 9,000 lb. per square inch.

129.—A bearing, similar to the one shown in Fig. 36 of the Text, is fastened to the frame of a machine by means of four ⅝-in. cap screws spaced equally on a 7-in. bolt circle. The bearing flange is 10 in. in diameter, and the load of 3,200 lb. is located 3½ in. from the frame. (*a*) Establish a formula for the maximum load coming upon any screw. (*b*) Determine the maximum tensile and shearing stresses coming upon any screw. (*c*) Assuming that two ½-in. dowel pins are used for relieving the cap screws from all shearing action, determine the magnitude of the shearing stress in the pins.

130.—A bearing, similar to the one shown in Fig. 36 of the Text, has flange and bolt circle diameters of 9 in. and 6½ in. respectively. The load coming on this bearing has a magnitude of 2,800 lb. and is located 3 in. from the frame. (*a*) Establish a formula for the maximum load coming upon any screw assuming four screws are used. (*b*) Determine the size of the cap screws required for this bearing, assuming the maximum permissible tensile and shearing stresses shall not exceed 8,000 and 6,000 lb. per square inch respectively. (*c*) Determine the size of the dowel pins required to relieve the cap screws from all shearing action, assuming an allowable shearing stress of 9,000 lb. per square inch.

131.—A bearing, similar to the one shown in Fig. 36 of the Text, is fastened to the frame of a machine by means of six ¾-in. cap screws spaced equally on an 11-in. bolt circle. The bearing flange is 14 in. in diameter and the load of 6,800 lb. is located 4 in. from the frame. (*a*) Establish a formula for the maximum load coming upon any screw. (*b*) Determine the maximum tensile and shearing stresses produced in any cap screw. (*c*) Assuming that the cap screws are relieved from all shearing action by the use of two ¾-in. dowel pins. determine the magnitude of the shearing stress in these pins.

132.—The pillar crane shown in Fig. 25 is fastened to the foundation by eight bolts spaced equally on a bolt circle, the diameter of which is $2b$. (a) Establish a formula for the maximum load coming upon any one bolt, assuming the diameter of the pillar flange is $2a$. (b) Determine the size of the foundation bolts, having given the following data: Load P is 5 tons; radius L is 16 ft.; diameters of the pillar flange and bolt circle are 72 in. and 64 in. respectively; allowable tensile stress is 10,000 lb. per square inch.

133.—The pillar crane shown in Fig. 25 is fastened to the foundation by 12 bolts spaced equally on a bolt circle, the diameter of which is $2b$. (a) Establish a formula for the maximum load coming upon any one bolt, assuming the diameter of the

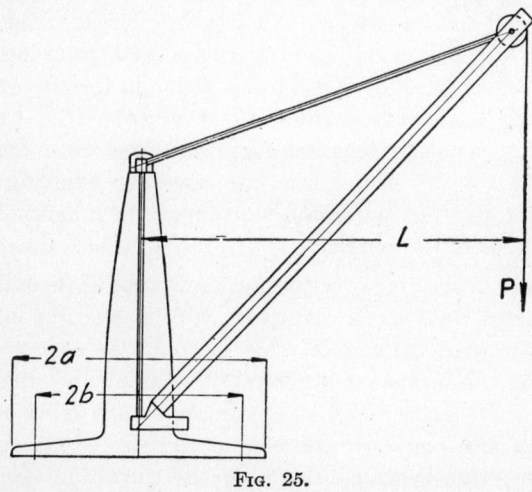

FIG. 25.

pillar flange is $2a$. (b) Determine the size of the foundation bolts, having given the following data: Load P is 8 tons; radius L is 18 ft.; diameters of the pillar flange and bolt circle are 84 in. and 72 in. respectively; permissible tensile stress is 12,000 lb. per square inch.

134.—The pillar crane shown in Fig. 25 is fastened to the foundation by 16 bolts spaced equally on a bolt circle, the diameter of which is $2b$. (a) Establish a formula for the maximum load coming upon any one bolt, assuming the diameter of the pillar flange is $2a$. (b) Determine the size of the foundation bolts, having given the following data: Load P is 10 tons; radius L is 20 ft.; diameters of the pillar flange and bolt circle are 84 in. and 72 in. respectively; permissible tensile stress is 12,000 lb. per square inch.

SECTION IV

COTTER AND PIN CONNECTIONS

135.—For the cotter joint shown in Fig. 47 of the Text establish empirical formulæ, in terms of d, for the dimensions of the various parts, assuming that no part of the joint is weaker than the rod and that the permissible shearing stress is equivalent to eight-tenths of the tensile stress or one-half of the bearing stress.

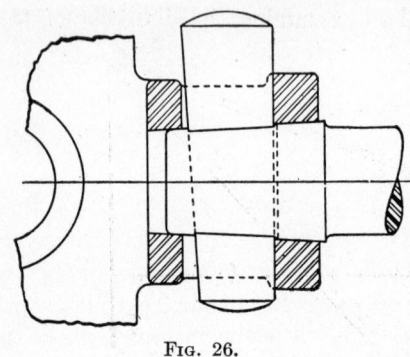

136 to 140.—Determine the dimensions of the various parts of a cotter joint, similar to the design shown in Fig. 26, used for fastening a piston rod to a cross head. Assume, for the particular case under discussion, the data given in Table 8 and that the joint be made approximately of uniform strength at all sections.

Fig. 26.

TABLE 8

	Problem number	136	137	138	139
1	Diameter of cylinder, inches	12	15	18	21
2	Steam pressure, pounds per square inch	150	150	165	165
3	Thickness of the cotter	0.3 of the diameter of the rod at the point where cotter is located			
4	Permissible tensile stress	7,500		9,000	
5	Permissible shearing stress	6,000		7,200	
6	Permissible bearing stress	12,000		14,400	

140 to 144.—It is required to determine the weakest part of the cottered bolt shown in Fig. 27, assuming, for the particular case considered, the data given in Table 9 and that the permissible tensile stress in the threaded part of the bolt is 8,000 lb. per square inch

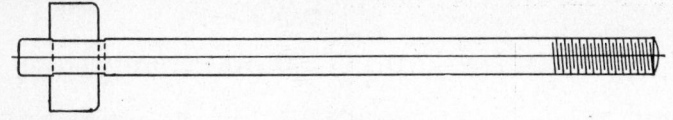

Fig. 27.

Table 9

		Problem number			
		140	141	142	143
1	Diameter of bolt, inches............	$1\frac{1}{2}$	$1\frac{3}{4}$	2	$2\frac{1}{2}$
2	Thickness of cotter, inches.........	$\frac{3}{8}$	$\frac{7}{16}$	$\frac{1}{2}$	$\frac{5}{8}$
3	Depth of cotter, inches.............	$1\frac{7}{8}$	$2\frac{1}{4}$	$2\frac{1}{2}$	$3\frac{1}{8}$
4	Length of cotter, inches............	$4\frac{1}{2}$	$5\frac{1}{4}$	6	$7\frac{1}{2}$
5	Distance from cotter to end of the bolt, inches.....................	$1\frac{1}{2}$	$1\frac{3}{4}$	2	$2\frac{1}{2}$

144.—For a $\frac{3}{8}$-in. adjustable rod and yoke and having the proportions given in Table 30, page 127 of the Text, determine the magnitude of the stresses induced in the various parts of the joint, assuming a permissible tensile stress of 10,000 lb. per square inch in the threaded rod used with this rod and yoke end.

145.—For a $\frac{1}{2}$-in. adjustable rod and yoke end having the proportions given in Table 30, page 127 of the Text, determine the magnitude of the stresses induced in the various parts of the joint, assuming a permissible tensile stress of 10,000 lb. per square inch in the threaded rod used with this rod and yoke end.

146.—Determine the magnitude of the stresses induced in the various parts of a No. 6 B. and S. drop-forged rod and yoke end, having the proportions given in Table 31, page 128 of the Text, assuming a permissible stress of 10,000 lb. per square inch in the shank.

147.—The statement of this problem is identical with that of Prob. 146, with the exception that a No. 7 B. and S. drop-forged rod and yoke end is to be used.

148.—The statement of this problem is identical with that of Prob. 146, with the exception that a No. 8 B. and S. drop-forged rod and yoke end is to be used.

149.—The statement of this problem is identical with that of Prob. 146, with the exception that a No. 9 B. and S. drop-forged rod and yoke end is to be used.

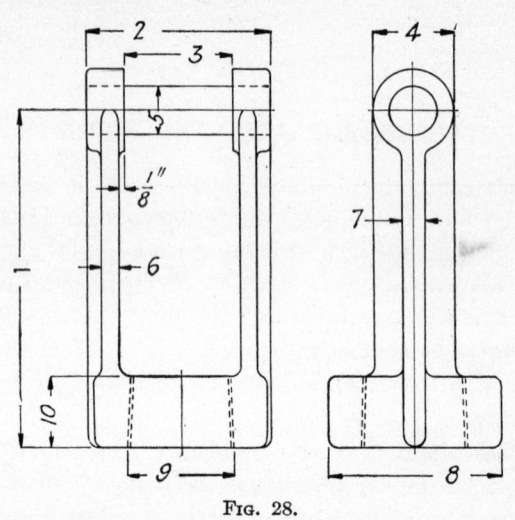

Fig. 28.

150 to 154.—Fig. 28 shows the design of a yoke, made of steel casting, and a cold-rolled steel sheave pin used in connection with a rope-geared air hoist. Using the data given in Table 10 for the particular yoke to be analyzed, it is required to determine the magnitude of the maximum stresses occurring in the various sections of the yoke and pin.

TABLE 10

Problem number		150	151	152	153
Pull on rod		2,380	4,350	10,300	26,900
Dimension number	1	7$\frac{1}{16}$	7 $\frac{5}{8}$	10 $\frac{1}{4}$	12$\frac{7}{8}$
	2	4	5 $\frac{1}{4}$	6 $\frac{1}{2}$	7$\frac{3}{4}$
	3	2$\frac{3}{8}$	3 $\frac{3}{8}$	4 $\frac{3}{8}$	5$\frac{3}{8}$
	4	1$\frac{3}{4}$	2 $\frac{1}{2}$	3 $\frac{1}{4}$	4
	5	1	1 $\frac{7}{16}$	1$\frac{15}{16}$	2$\frac{7}{16}$
	6	$\frac{3}{8}$	$\frac{7}{16}$	$\frac{9}{16}$	$\frac{3}{4}$
	7	$\frac{1}{2}$	$\frac{5}{8}$	$\frac{3}{4}$	1
	8	3$\frac{3}{4}$	4 $\frac{3}{4}$	5 $\frac{1}{2}$	6$\frac{3}{4}$
	9	2$\frac{5}{16}$	2$\frac{13}{16}$	3 $\frac{7}{16}$	3$\frac{7}{8}$
	10	1$\frac{1}{2}$	1 $\frac{5}{8}$	2	2$\frac{3}{8}$

SECTION V

CYLINDERS, PLATES AND SPRINGS

154.—Determine the minimum thickness of the walls of a cast-iron cylinder 8 in. in diameter, subjected to an internal pressure of 750 lb. per square inch, assuming closed ends and that the maximum allowable tensile stress is 2,500 lb. per square inch. Use Lamé's as well as Clavarino's formula.

155.—The statement of this problem is identical with that of Prob. 154, with the exception that the diameter of the cylinder is 10 in.

156.—The statement of this problem is identical with that of Prob. 154, with the exception that the diameter of the cylinder is 12 in., the internal pressure is 600 lb. per square inch and the allowable stress is 2,000 lb. per square inch.

157.—A steel casting cylinder 15 in. in diameter and having closed ends is subjected to an internal pressure of 2,500 lb. per square inch. Determine the minimum thickness of the walls, assuming a maximum allowable tensile stress of 10,000 lb. per square inch and using (*a*) Lamé's formula; (*b*) Clavarino's formula.

158.—The statement of this problem is identical with that of Prob. 157, with the exception that the diameter of the cylinder is 20 in. and the internal pressure is 1,500 lb. per square inch.

159.—The statement of this problem is identical with that of Prob. 157, with the exception that the diameter of the cylinder is 24 in. and the internal pressure is 1,200 lb. per square inch.

160.—Using Lamé's as well as Clavarino's formula, determine the maximum tangential stress produced in the walls of a cast-iron cylinder whose outside and inside diameters are 20 in. and 16 in. respectively, the internal pressure being 250 lb. per square inch.

161.—A hydraulic press cylinder, made of steel casting and subjected to an internal pressure of 2,500 lb. per square inch, has an inside diameter of $21\frac{1}{2}$ in. and a wall thickness of $2\frac{3}{4}$ in.

Using Lamé's and Clavarino's formulas, determine the maximum tangential stress produced in the walls of the cylinder.

162.—On a 400-ton hydraulic baling press the cylinder, made of steel casting and subjected to an internal pressure of 4,000 lb. per square inch, has an inside diameter of 17½ in. and a wall thickness of 2⅝ in. Determine the maximum tangential stress produced in the walls, using Lamé's and Clavarino's formula.

163.—Determine the maximum tangenital stress produced in the walls of a cast-iron cylinder having an inside diameter of 36 in. and a wall thickness of 2 in. Use Lamé's and Clavarino's formulas, assuming the cylinder is subjected to an internal pressure of 150 lb. per square inch.

164.—(a) Determine the thickness of the cast-iron steam-chest cover on an engine cylinder, having given the following data: Steam pressure is 150 lb. per square inch; allowable stress is 3,500 lb. per square inch; inside dimensions of the chest are 16 by 12 in. (b) Determine the probable number and size of the studs that would be used for fastening the steam-chest cover, assuming an allowable stress of 5,000 lb. per square inch in the studs.

165.—Determine the minimum thickness of the cast-iron heads for the cylinder described in Prob. 160, assuming one head to be firmly fastened to the cylinder by means of bolts while the other is cast integral with the cylinder. Assume the maximum allowable stress as 4,500 lb. per square inch and the radius of the corner fillet on the cast head as 2½ in.

166.—(a) Determine the minimum thickness of the cast-iron heads for the cylinder described in Prob. 156, assuming the heads to be firmly fastened to the cylinder by means of studs and the maximum allowable stress to be 5,000 lb. per square inch. (b) If the thickness of the heads is made 1½ in., determine the maximum stress in the heads and the maximum deflection assuming $E = 14,000,000$. (c) Determine the probable number and size of the studs that would be used for fastening the heads, assuming an allowable stress of 5,000 lb. per square inch.

167.—(a) A cast-iron cylinder head, 1½ in. thick, is fastened to a 10-in. cylinder by means of cap screws. Determine the pressure that may be carried in the cylinder assuming the maximum allowable stress in the head to be 5,000 lb. per square inch. (b) Assuming $E = 12,000,000$, what will be the probable deflection of the head? (c) Determine the probable number and size of the cap screws that would be used for fastening the heads, assuming an allowable stress of 6,000 lb. per square inch.

168.—(a) Determine the minimum thickness of the steel casting head for the cylinder described in Prob. 161, assuming the head to be cast integral with the cylinder. The maximum allowable stress may be taken as 15,000 lb. per square inch and the radius of the corner fillet as 3 in. (b) If the head were fastened to the cylinder by means of cap screws, what would be its thickness? (c) How many and what size of cap screws would you advise using, assuming an allowable stress of 20,000 lb. per square inch? (d) Does a detachable head give a practical design in this case?

169.—(a) For the cylinder described in Prob. 162, determine the minimum thickness of the head assuming it is cast integral with the cylinder. The maximum allowable stress may be taken as 16,000 lb. per square inch and the radius of the corner fillet as 3 in. (b) What is the thickness of the head, if it were fastened to the cylinder by means of cap screws? (c) Determine the probable number and size of the cap screws that you would advise using assuming an allowable stress of 20,000 lb. per square inch. (d) Do you consider the detachable head a good design in this case?

170.—In a multiple disk clutch, the pressure between the disks is produced by a helical type of compression spring having 7.75 coils of $\frac{1}{2}$-in. steel wire, the outer diameter of the coils being 6 in. The free length of the spring is 8 in. and when in place with the clutch engaged, the length is 5 in. Determine the total axial pressure between the clutch plates and the torsional stress produced in the spring.

171.—A helical type of compression spring having 9.5 coils of $\frac{3}{8}$-in. steel wire is used for producing the axial pressure in a multiple disk clutch. The outer diameter of the coils is $3\frac{1}{8}$ in., the free length is $7\frac{1}{4}$ in., and with the clutch engaged the length is $5\frac{1}{8}$ in. Determine the total pressure exerted by the spring and the torsional stress produced in the spring.

172.—A compression spring of the helical type, consisting of 6.5 turns of $\frac{1}{4}$ by $\frac{9}{32}$ in. steel wire, is used for producing the pressure between the two cones of a clutch. The outer diameter of the coils is $2\frac{5}{16}$ in., the free length is $4\frac{7}{16}$ in., and when in place with the clutch engaged, the length is $2\frac{15}{16}$ in. Determine the total pressure exerted by the spring and the torsional stress produced in the material.

173.—The spring for a cam-operated oil-pump plunger, is made up of No. 12 (0.1055-in.) steel wire and consists of 4.5 effective coils having an outer diameter of $^{27}\!/_{32}$ in. The free length is 1.032 in. and when the spring exerts a pressure of $28\frac{1}{2}$ lb. upon the plunger, the compressed length is 0.725 in. Determine the magnitude of the torsional stress produced in the material, also the probable magnitude of the torsional modulus of elasticity.

174.—A compression spring is made of $\frac{5}{8}$-in round steel and consists of 10 effective coils having an outer diameter of $2\frac{7}{8}$ in. The free length is $8\frac{1}{4}$ in. and when compressed solid, the length is $6\frac{9}{16}$ in. The load required for the maximum deflection is 3,500. (a) Determine the magnitude of the torsional stress produced in the material, also the probable magnitude of the torsional modulus of elasticity. (b) Determine the load and the torsional stress corresponding to a length of spring of 7 in.

175.—A compression spring, made of $\frac{7}{8}$-in. round steel, has 5.5 effective coils having an outer diameter of $4\frac{1}{8}$ in. The free length is $6^{13}\!/_{16}$ in. and when compressed solid, the length is $5\frac{1}{4}$ in. The load required to produce the latter condition is 7,000 lb. (a) Determine the magnitude of the torsional stress produced in the material, also the probable magnitude of the torsional modulus of elasticity. (b) Determine the load and the torsional stress corresponding to a length of spring of 6 in.

176.—A compression spring, made of 1-in. round steel, has 5.25 effective coils having an outer diameter of $4\frac{5}{8}$ in. The free length is 7.5 in. and when compressed solid, the length is $5\frac{3}{4}$ in. The load required to produce the latter condition is 10,060 lb. (a) Determine the magnitude of the torsional stress produced in the material, also the probable magnitude of the torsional modulus of elasticity. (b) If the load on the spring is 6,000 lb., determine the corresponding torsional stress and length of the spring.

177.—A compression spring, made of $1\frac{3}{16}$-in. round steel, has five effective coils having an outer diameter of $5\frac{7}{16}$ in. The free length is $8\frac{1}{4}$ in. and when compressed solid, the length is $6\frac{9}{16}$ in. The load required to produce the latter condition is 12,500 lb. (a) Determine the magnitude of the torsional stress produced in the material, also the probable magnitude of the torsional modulus of elasticity. (b) If the load on the spring is 8,000 lb., determine the corresponding torsional stress and length of the spring.

178.—A compression spring, made of $1\tfrac{9}{16}$-in. round steel, has 3.25 effective coils having an outer diameter of 8 in. The free length is $7\tfrac{7}{8}$ in. and when compressed solid, the length is $5\tfrac{3}{4}$ in. The load required to produce the latter condition is 20,300 lb. (a) Determine the magnitude of the torsional stress produced in the material, also the probable magnitude of the torsional modulus of elasticity. (b) If the load on the spring is 12,000 lb., determine the corresponding torsional stress and length of the spring.

179.—A compression spring, made of $1\tfrac{3}{8}$-in. round steel, has 3.5 effective coils having an outer diameter of 7 in. The free length is $7\tfrac{1}{8}$ in. and when compressed solid, the length is $5\tfrac{1}{4}$ in. The load required to produce the latter condition is 15,530 lb. (a) Determine the magnitude of the torsional stress produced in the material, also the probable magnitude of the torsional modulus of elasticity. (b) Determine the load and the torsional stress corresponding to a length of spring of 6 in.

180.—The spring described in Prob. 174 is used in conjunction with that described in Prob. 177 to form a concentric helical spring. (a) Determine, for each spring, the loads corresponding to compressed spring lengths of 7, 7.5 and 8 in. (b) For each of the springs show by means of a graph how the load varies with the length of the spring, letting the ordinates represent the load in pounds and the abscissæ the spring lengths in inches. (c) In a similar manner, plot a graph showing the combined action of the two springs.

181.—A concentric helical spring is made by placing the spring described in Prob. 175 inside of the spring described in Prob. 179. (a) For each spring, determine the loads corresponding to compressed spring lengths of 5.5, 6 and 6.5 in. (b) By means of a graph, show for each of the springs how the load varies with the length of the spring, using the loads in pounds as ordinates and the spring lengths in inches as abscissæ. (c) In a similar manner, plot a graph showing the combined action of the two springs.

182.—A concentric helical spring is formed by using the springs described in Probs. 176 and 178. (a) For each spring, determine the loads corresponding to compressed spring lengths of 6, 6.5 and 7 in. (b) By means of a graph, show for each of the springs how the load varies with the length of the spring, using the loads in pounds as ordinates and the spring lengths in inches as abscissæ. (c) In a similar manner, plot a graph showing the combined action of the two springs.

SECTION VI

BELTING

183.—A flywheel, 72 in. in diameter running at 240 r.p.m., is connected, by a leather belt having cemented joints, to a pulley 18 in. in diameter. Determine the width of the double belt required to transmit 100 hp., assuming the thickness as 0.35 in. and the distance between the shafts as 18 ft. What is the length of the belt?

184.—Two pulleys, 18 in. in diameter running 350 r.p.m., are connected by a crossed leather belt ⅜ in. thick and 4 in. wide having wire-laced joints. If the distance between the shafts is 9.5 ft., what horsepower will the belt transmit? Determine the length of the belt.

185.—Two pulleys, 30 in. in diameter running 300 r.p.m., are connected by a crossed leather belt $5/16$ in. thick having cemented joints. If the distance between the shafts is 12 ft., what width of belt is required to transmit 35 hp.? Determine the length of the belt.

186.—A corliss engine, having a 14-ft. flywheel, transmits 150 hp. at 68 r.p.m. to a pulley 56 in. in diameter by means of a double leather belt ⅜ in. thick. The distance between the shafts is 20 ft. 4 in. Assuming cemented joints are used, determine the width and length of the belt required for this transmission.

187.—A corliss engine having a 18-ft. flywheel, transmits 300 hp. at 75 r.p.m. to a pulley 68 in. in diameter by means of a double leather belt ⅜ in. thick. The distance between the shafts is 23 ft. 9 in. Assuming cemented joints are used, determine the width and length of the belt required for this transmission.

188.—A 100-hp. corliss engine, running at 95 r.p.m. and having an 8-ft. flywheel, is connected to a 42-in. pulley by means of a double leather belt ⅜ in. thick. The distance between the shafts is 23.5 ft. Assuming cemented joints are used, determine the width and length of the belt required for this transmission.

189.—A 35-hp. motor, running at 1,720 r.p.m., is connected to a 24-in. pulley by means of a leather belt $7/32$ in. thick. The diameter of the motor pulley is 8 in. and the distance between the shafts is 21 ft. 8 in. Assuming cemented joints are used, determine the width and length of the belt required for this drive.

190.—Two pulleys, 24-in. in diameter running at 370 r.p.m., are connected by a crossed leather belt $3/8$ in. thick having wire-laced joints. If the belt transmits 30 hp. and the distance between the shafts is 10 ft., what width and length of belt is required?

191.—In a certain mill a corliss engine, running at 85 r.p.m. and having a flywheel 18 ft. in diameter, transmits 2,000 hp. to a pulley 8 ft. 6 in. in diameter by means of a triple leather belt 96 in. wide and $3/4$ in. thick weighing 3,500 lb. The distance between the shafts is approximately 39 ft. Determine the unit weight of the belt and the probable coefficient of friction between the belt and pulley, assuming that a cemented joint is used.

192.—(a) A high-speed engine, having a flywheel 66 in. in diameter, is connected by a single leather belt to a generator having a 17-in. pulley. The engine is capable of developing 65 hp. at 260 r.p.m., and the distance between the shafts is 16 ft. Determine the required width of the belt, assuming its thickness as $7/32$ in. and that a cemented joint is used. (b) By installing a Lenix tension pulley the distance between the shafts, in the above installation, may be decreased from 16 ft. to 6.5 ft. and at the same time the angles of contact on the flywheel and the generator pulley are increased to 242 deg. and 251 deg. respectively. Determine the width of the single leather belt required for this installation. (c) Determine the probable loss in power due to the Lenix drive assuming 5 hp. represents the loss in the original installation.

193.—A 250-hp. motor, running at 500 r.p.m., transmits power to a large stone crusher by means of a double leather belt 30 in. wide and $3/8$ in. thick. The motor pulley is 30 in. in diameter and the crusher pulley 120 in. in diameter. By means of a Lenix tension pulley, the angle of contact on the motor pulley is made approximately 235 deg. Using Barth's formula for the probable coefficient of friction, determine the stress in the belt.

194.—A 5-hp. motor, running at 1,140 r.p.m., drives a line shaft by means of a leather belt 4 in. wide and $5/32$ in. thick. The motor and the line shaft pulleys are 5½ in. and 42 in. in diameter respectively. Due to the short distance between the shafts, a Lenix tension pulley is used giving an angle of contact approximating 215 deg. on the motor pulley and 234 deg. on the line shaft pulley. Assuming the belt has cemented joints, determine the probable coefficient of friction existing in this installation.

195.—(a) The 12-ft. flywheel of a 350-hp. corliss engine running at 100 r.p.m., is connected to a 63-in. pulley by means of a double leather belt 30 in. wide and $7/16$ in. thick having cemented joints. The line shaft, to which the driven pulley is keyed, is located 11 ft. in front of the engine shaft and 11 ft. 7 in. above it. Determine the probable horsepower that the belt will transmit, assuming the coefficient of friction as 0.45.

(b) The above installation gave considerable trouble so a Lenix tension pulley was installed thereby increasing the angle of contact on the driven pulley to approximately 215 deg. Determine the horsepower that the belt is now capable of transmitting.

196.—A 75-hp. motor, running at 950 r.p.m., is connected to an air compressor by means of a double leather belt 10 in. wide and $9/32$ in. thick. The diameter of the motor pulley is 14½ in. and that of the compressor pulley is 64 in. Due to the short distance of 6 ft. 2½ in. between the shafts, a Lenix tension pulley is used, thus giving 227 deg. as the angle of contact on the motor pulley. Assume the belt has cemented joints and that its strength per square inch of area is as given in the Text; determine the probable coefficient of friction and compare this value with that obtained by the Barth formula.

197.—A 50-hp. motor, running at 1,120 r.p.m., is connected to a rotary kiln in a cement works by means of a single leather belt 10 in. wide and $7/32$ in. thick. The diameter of the motor pulley is 12 in. and that of the driven pulley is 10 ft. Due to the short distance of 8 ft. 3 in. between the shafts, a Lenix tension pulley is used, thus giving 225 deg. as the angle of contact on the motor pulley. Assuming the belt has cemented joints and that its strength per square inch of area is as given in the Text; determine the probable coefficient of friction and compare this value with that obtained by the Barth formula.

198.—A 35-hp. motor, running at 575 r.p.m., is connected to an air compressor by means of a double leather belt 8 in. wide and

9/32 in. thick. The diameter of the motor pulley is 14 in. and that of the compressor flywheel is 66 in. Due to the short distance of 60 in. between the shafts, a Lenix tension pulley is used, thus giving 230 deg. as the angle of contact on the motor pulley. Assuming the belt has cemented joints and that its strength per square inch of area is as given in the text, determine the probable coefficient of friction and compare this value with that obtained by the Barth formula.

199.—A 150-hp. corliss engine, running at 85 r.p.m., is connected to a 100-kw. generator by means of a double leather belt 12 in. wide and 3/8 in. thick. The diameter of the flywheel is 14 ft. and that of the generator pulley is 22 in. The distance between the shafts is 14 ft. and by means of a Lenix tension pulley, the angle of contact on the generator pulley is made 228 deg. Assuming the belt has cemented joints and that its strength per square inch of area is as given in the Text, determine the probable coefficient of friction and compare this value with that obtained by the Barth formula.

200.—(a) Two pulleys 18 in. in diameter, running at 250 r.p.m. are connected by a crossed leather belt 11/32 in. thick having hand-laced wire joints. What width of belt is necessary to transmit 10 hp. assuming the distance between the shafts is 12 ft.? (b) What length of belt is required for the transmission?

201.—A motor, running at 1,730 r.p.m., delivers 10 hp. to a line shaft by means of a 5 in. by 4 ply (0.24 in. thick) rubber belt. The motor and line-shaft pulleys are 5 in. and 48 in. in diameter respectively and the distance between the shafts is 13 ft. 4 in. Determine the probable working stress produced in the belt, also its length.

202.—A 5-in. by 4-ply (0.24 in. thick) rubber belt connects a 25-hp. motor, running at 1,700 r.p.m., to a line shaft. The motor and line-shaft pulleys are 8 in. and 28 in. respectively and the distance between the shafts is 8.5 ft. Determine the probable working stress produced in the belt, also its length.

203.—A blower, requiring 26 hp. at 2,800 r.p.m., is driven from a countershaft by means of a 4-in. by 5-ply (0.29 in. thick) rubber belt. The driving and driven pulleys are 30 in. and 5 in. in diameter respectively and the distance between the shafts is 26 ft. Determine the probable working stress produced in the belt, also its length.

BELTING

204.—A 100-hp. corliss engine running at 85 r.p.m. and having an 8-ft. flywheel, is connected to a 42-in. pulley by means of an 18-in. by 7-ply (0.39 in. thick) rubber belt. The distance between the shafts is 23.5 ft. Determine the probable working stress produced in the belt, also its length.

205.—A 35-hp. motor, running at 1,720 r.p.m. and having an 8-in. pulley, is connected to a line-shaft pulley 24 in. in diameter by o 4-ply (0.24 in. thick) rubber belt. The distance between the shafts is 21 ft. 8 in. Determine the width and length of the belt required for this transmission.

206.—A 150-hp. corliss engine, running at 68 r.p.m. and having a 14-ft. flywheel, is connected to a line-shaft pulley 4 ft. 8 in. in diameter by a 6-ply (0.34 in. thick) rubber belt. If the distance between the shafts is 20 ft. 4 in., what width and length of belt is required for this transmission?

207.—A 300-hp. corliss engine, running at 75 r.p.m. and having an 18-ft. flywheel, is connected to a line-shaft pulley 5 ft. 8 in. in diameter by a 6-ply (0.34 in. thick) rubber belt. If the distance between the shafts is 23.75 ft., what width and length of belt is required for this transmission?

208.—A 7.5-hp. motor, running at 1,725 r.p.m. and having a 5-in. pulley, is connected to a line-shaft pulley 30 in. in diameter by a 4-ply (0.24 in. thick) rubber belt. If the distance between the shafts is 6 ft. 11 in., what width and length of belt is required for this transmission?

209.—A 450-hp. engine, having a flywheel 15 ft. 2 in. in diameter and running at 70 r.p.m., is connected to a pulley 12 ft. 7½ in. in diameter by means of two 8-in. steel belts. Having given the distance between the shafts as 40.25 ft., determine the working stress in the belt assuming the thickness as 0.8 mm., and that the coefficient of friction is 0.4.

210.—In a textile mill 250 hp. is transmitted from the engine to a drive shaft by means of an 8-in. steel belt. The flywheel on the engine is 12 ft. 2 in. in diameter and runs at 80 r.p.m., while the pulley on the drive shaft is 9 ft. in diameter. Determine the thickness of the belt, having given the distance between the shaft centers as 34.25 ft., assuming a safe working stress of 16,000 lb. per square inch and a coefficient of friction of 0.4.

211.—In a textile mill a 6-in. steel belt, running at 2,800 ft. per minute, is used to transmit 70 hp. The pulleys used in the transmission are 54 in. and 49¼ in. in diameter, and their shafts are 29 ft. apart. Determine the thickness of this belt, assuming a safe working stress of 15,000 lb. per square inch and a coefficient of friction of 0.4.

212.—A 22-hp. engine, having a 42-in. flywheel and running at 250 r.p.m., is connected to a generator by means of a 4-in. steel belt. The generator pulley is 21 in. in diameter and the distance between the shaft centers is 10.5 ft. Determine the working stress in the belt, assuming the thickness as 0.3 mm., and that the coefficient of friction is 0.4.

SECTION VII

ROPE TRANSMISSION

213.—On a derrick equipped with a block and tackle reefed with manila rope, the hook block contains two sheaves while the block at the end of the boom has three sheaves. Determine the following: (a) The size of rope required to hoist a load of 10,000 lb., assuming a minimum factor of safety of seven. (b) The efficiency of the block and tackle.

214.—A block and tackle, having three sheaves on each of the blocks, is reefed with a 1¼-in. manila rope. Determine the capacity of the block and tackle, basing it on a factor of safety of six. What is the efficiency?

215.—A block and tackle, having three sheaves on each of the blocks, is reefed with 1¾-in. manila rope. Determine the capacity of the block and tackle, basing it on a factor of safety of six. What is the efficiency?

216.—A block and tackle, having three sheaves on the hook block and four at the top, is reefed with 2-in. manila rope. Determine the capacity of the block and tackle, basing it on a factor of safety of six. What is the efficiency?

217.—On a derrick equipped with a block and tackle reefed with manila rope, the hook block as well as that at the end of the boom contains three sheaves. Determine the following: (a) The size of rope required to hoist a load of 12,000 lb., assuming a minimum factor of safety of six. (b) The efficiency of the block and tackle.

218.—A block and tackle, having four sheaves on each of the blocks, is reefed with 1½-in. manila rope. Determine the capacity of the block and tackle, basing it on a factor of safety of six. What is the efficiency?

219.—On a derrick equipped with a block and tackle reefed with manila rope, the hook block contains three sheaves while the block at the end of the boom has four sheaves. Determine the following: (a) The size of rope required to hoist 14,000 lb., assuming a minimum factor of safety of six. (*b*) The efficiency of the block and tackle.

220.—In a cotton mill nine manila ropes are used to transmit 400 hp. at 75 r.p.m. of the driving sheave. The diameters of the driving and driven sheaves are 21 ft. and 64 in. respectively and the distance between the shafts is 76 ft. (*a*) If the Allis standard groove is used, what size of rope is required? (*b*) What is the length of each rope?

221.—Twelve manila ropes are used for transmitting 300 hp. at a speed of 4,200 ft. per minute. Assuming the arc of contact as 165 deg. and the Allis standard groove, determine the following. (*a*) The size of rope required. (*b*) The maximum horsepower the size of rope selected will transmit and the velocity corresponding to this horsepower.

222.—Fifteen manila ropes are used for transmitting 270 hp. at a speed of 4,500 ft. per minute. Assuming the arc of contact as 180 deg. and the Allis standard groove, determine the size of rope required. (*b*) Determine the maximum horsepower this size of rope will transmit and the velocity corresponding to this horsepower.

223.—A 16-ft. flywheel, running at 80 r.p.m., is connected to a sheave 8 ft. in diameter by means of thirty manila ropes. What size of rope is required to transmit 1,500 hp., assuming the distance between the shafts as 48 ft. and that the Dodge standard groove is used?

224.—A 300-hp. alternating-current motor, running at 430 r.p.m., is connected to the pinion shaft of a mine hoist by means of thirty-two 1-in. manila ropes. The sheave on the motor shaft is 44 in. in diameter and that on the pinion shaft is 13 ft. Determine the stress per rope, assuming the distance between the shafts is 36 ft. and that the sheave grooves are similar to the Allis standard.

225.—In a direct rope drive six 1-in. manila ropes are used to transmit 150 hp. at 156 r.p.m. of the 60-in. sheaves. The distance between the shafts is 50 ft. and the grooves are the Dodge standard type. Determine the probable coefficient of friction existing between the rope and the sides of the groove, assuming the loose tension per rope is 180 lb.

226.—A 15-ft. flywheel, running at 90 r.p.m., is connected to a sheave 7 ft. in diameter by means of 24 manila ropes. What size of rope is required to transmit 750 hp., assuming the distance between the shafts as 60 ft. and that the Allis standard groove is used?

227.—An electric motor delivers 1,000 hp. at 375 r.p.m. to a jack shaft used for driving two large pulp-wood grinders. The transmission consists of an American system of manila-rope drive

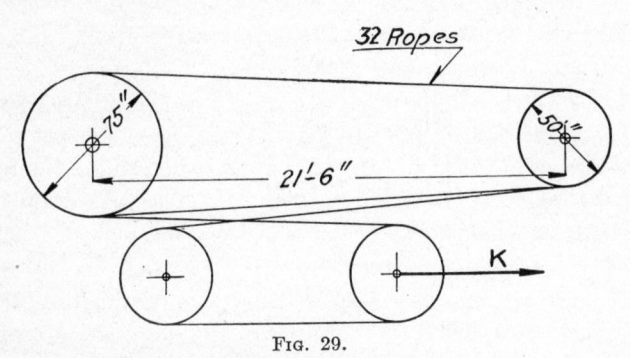

Fig. 29.

similar to that shown in Fig. 29. The motor sheave is 50 in. in diameter and that on the jack shaft is 75 in. in diameter. Determine the size of the rope and the magnitude of the force K required on the tension carriage, assuming the grooves on the sheaves are the Dodge standard.

228.—A rolling mill is driven by means of thirty 1¾-in. manila ropes. The diameter of the driving sheave is 76½ in. and that of the driven sheave is 20 ft. If the distance between the shafts is 42 ft. and assuming the normal working tension of the rope as given in the Text, determine the probable magnitude of the coefficient of friction for the two types of grooves used in rope drives.

229.—A 750-hp. tandem compound engine, capable of delivering 970 hp. at 150 r.p.m., furnishes power to a drive shaft by means of an American system of manila-rope drive similar to that shown in Fig. 30. The driving sheave on the engine is 120 in. in diameter and has 22 grooves. The driven sheave is 90 in. in diameter and has 22 grooves. Assuming the grooves are similar

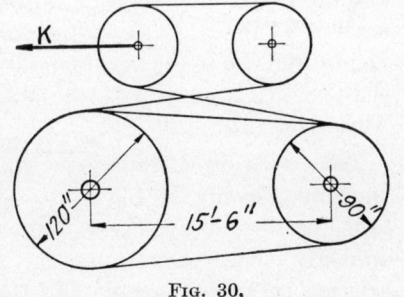

Fig. 30.

to the Allis standard, determine the size of rope required, also the magnitude of the force K required on the tension carriage.

230.—In a cotton mill an American system of manila-rope drive is used for transmitting 500 hp. between two shafts located 54 in. apart as shown in Fig. 31. Determine the following, assuming that the Dodge type of groove is used: (a) Size of the rope. (b) The magnitude of the force K required on the tension carriage.

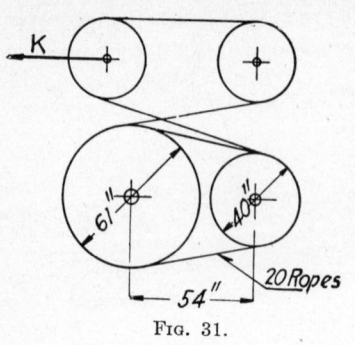

Fig. 31.

231.—The American system of manila-rope transmission shown in Fig. 32 is used for transmitting equal power to each of four parallel shafts in a large flour mill. If a $1\frac{1}{4}$-in. manila rope is used and the sheaves are provided with the Dodge standard groove, determine the following: (a) The total horsepower transmitted by the driver assuming it

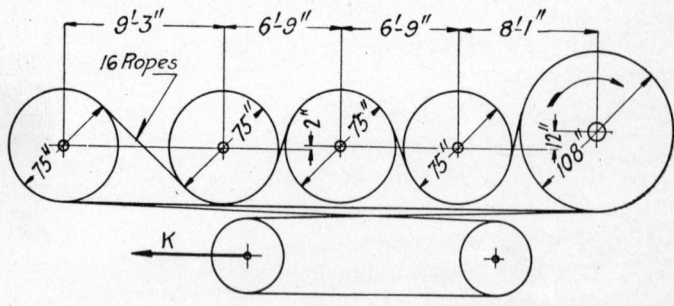

Fig. 32.

makes 160 r.p.m. (b) The tension in the ropes at each of the driven sheaves. (c) The magnitude of the force K required on the tension carriage.

232.—A block and tackle, having three sheaves on the hook block and four at the top, is reefed with $\frac{1}{2}$ in. 6 by 19 plow-steel wire rope. Assuming the sheaves are 10 in. in diameter, determine the capacity of the block and tackle, basing it on a factor of safety of three. What is the efficiency?

233.—A block and tackle, having four sheaves on each of the blocks is reefed with $\frac{5}{8}$-in. 6 by 19 plow-steel wire rope. Assuming the sheaves are 12 in. in diameter, determine the capacity of the block and tackle, basing it on a factor of safety of three. What is the efficiency?

234.—A block and tackle, having three sheaves on each of the blocks, is reefed with ¾-in. 6 by 19 crucible-steel wire rope. Assuming the sheaves are 14 in. in diameter, determine the capacity of the block and tackle, basing it on a factor of safety of three. What is the efficiency?

235.—In a block and tackle, reefed with plow-steel wire rope, each block contains three sheaves 9 in. in diameter. Determine the following: (*a*) The size of rope required to hoist a load of 2 tons, assuming a factor of safety of four. (*b*) The efficiency of the block and tackle.

236.—In a block and tackle, reefed with extra flexible plow-steel wire rope, each block contains four sheaves 10 in. in diameter. Determine the following: (*a*) The size of rope required to hoist a load of 4 tons, assuming a factor of safety of four. (*b*) The efficiency of the block and tackle.

237.—On a derrick, equipped with a block and tackle reefed with plow-steel wire rope, the hook block contains two 12-in. sheaves while the block at the end of the boom has three 12-in. sheaves. Determine the following: (*a*) The size of rope required to hoist a load of 5 tons assuming a factor of safety of four. (*b*) The efficiency of the block and tackle.

238.—In a hydraulic elevator of the inverted plunger type, similar to the one shown in Fig. 33, the plunger is 8 in. in diameter. Assuming a water pressure of 750 lb. per square inch and that

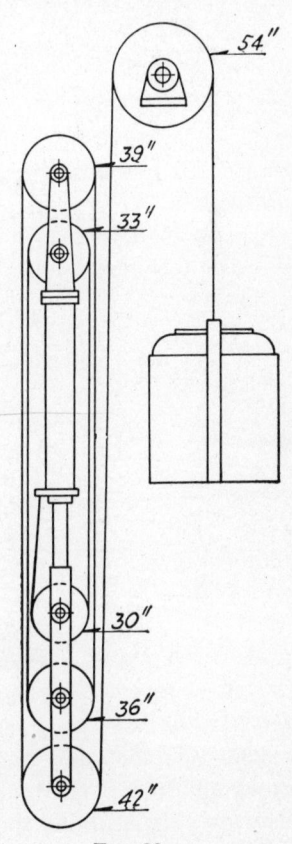

Fig. 33.

six ⅝-in. 6 by 19 plow-steel wire ropes are used, determine the following: (*a*) The load that can be raised assuming the efficiency of the cylinder is 85 per cent. (*b*) The apparent factor of safety used for the ropes. (*c*) The loads on the pins supporting the movable sheaves. (*d*) The overall efficiency of the elevator.

239.—On a derrick, equipped with a block and tackle reefed with ⅝-in. 6 by 19 crucible-steel wire rope, the hook block as well as the block at the end of the boom contains four 9½-in. sheaves. Determine the following, assuming the capacity of the block is 15 tons: (*a*) The factor of safety used in arriving at the size of the rope. (*b*) The efficiency of the block and tackle. (*c*) If the bore of the sheave bushing is 1½ in. and the length is 2 in., determine the maximum bearing pressure coming upon any one sheave.

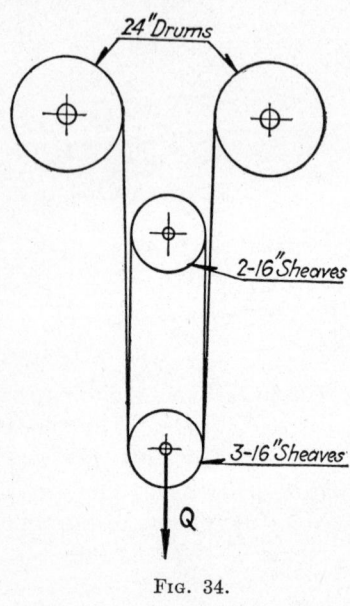

240.—Determine the magnitude of the load Q that may be raised by means of the double-drum crane-trolley hoisting gear shown in Fig. 34, assuming a factor of safety of four for the ¾-in. 6 by 19 plow-steel wire rope used in reefing the block. What is the efficiency of the block and tackle?

FIG. 34.

241.—A block and tackle, rated at 40 tons, is reefed with ¾-in. 6 by 19 plow-steel wire rope. Four 13¼ in. sheaves are used on both the top and bottom blocks. Determine the following: (*a*) The factor of safety used in arriving at the size of the rope. (*b*) The efficiency of the block and tackle. (*c*) If the length of the sheave hub is 2 in. and the bore 2 in., what is the maximum bearing pressure coming upon any one sheave?

242.—In a 7½-ton monorail hoist, a ½ in. 6 by 19 plow-steel wire rope leads from the 12-in. hoisting drum down around the sheave on the hook block, then up around a fixed guide sheave and finally is anchored to the hook block. Assuming all of the sheaves are 10 in. in diameter, determine the following: (*a*) The factor of safety used in arriving at the size of the rope. (*b*) The efficiency of the block and tackle.

243.—(*a*) Determine the size of the cylinder and the number of ⅝-in. 6 by 19 plow-steel wire ropes required for a low-pressure pulling type of hydraulic elevator similar to that shown in

Fig. 35, having given the following data: (1) The load Q to be raised is 4,000 lb. (2) The water pressure is 100 lb. per square inch. (3) The efficiency of the hydraulic cylinder is 75 per cent. (4) The factor of safety for the ropes is eight. (b) What is the overall efficiency of the elevator?

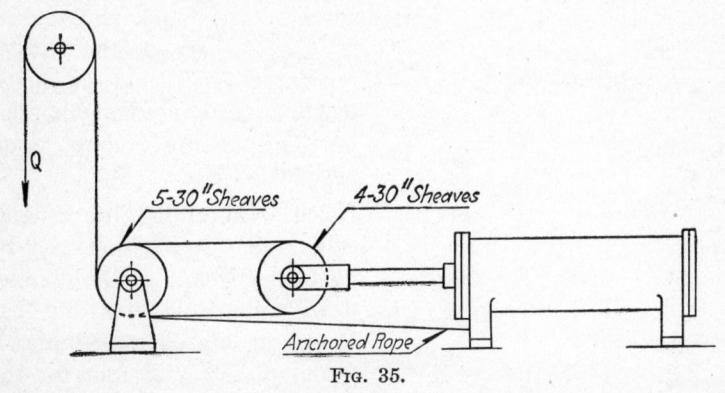

Fig. 35.

244.—In a 5-ton monorail hoist, the hook block contains two 8-in. sheaves and the fixed block has one sheave. The blocks and drum are reefed with ⅜-in. 6 by 19 plow-steel wire rope. Assuming that C for a ⅜-in. rope is 1.09, determine the following: (a) The factor of safety used in arriving at the size of the rope. (b) The efficiency of the block and tackle.

SECTION VIII

CHAIN TRANSMISSION

245.—In a crane, equipped with a block and tackle containing two 10-in. sheaves in each block, ½-in. coil chain is used for hoisting the load. Determine the capacity and the efficiency of the block and tackle, assuming the following data. The diameter of the sheave pin is 2¼ in.; the coefficients of chain and journal friction are 0.2 and 0.08 respectively.

246.—In a block and tackle, reefed with ⅜-in. coil chain, two sheaves are used in the hook block and three in the upper block. Each of the sheaves is 8 in. in diameter and is mounted on a 1¾-in. pin. If the coefficients of chain and journal friction are 0.2 and 0.08 respectively, what is the capacity of the block? What is the efficiency?

247.—In a block and tackle, reefed with ⅝-in coil chain, three sheaves are used in each block. Each of the sheaves is 12 in. in diameter and is mounted on a 2½-in. pin. If the coefficients of chain and journal friction are 0.2 and 0.08 respectively, what is the capacity of the block? What is the efficiency?

248.—Determine the size of coil chain required to hoist a load of 5 tons by means of a block and tackle, each block of which contains two sheaves. The factor of safety should not be less than five and the value of K may be assumed as 1.06. What is the efficiency of the block and tackle?

249.—Determine the size of coil chain required to hoist a load of 15 tons by means of a block and tackle, each block of which contains three sheaves. The factor of safety should not be less than five and the value of K may be assumed as 1.07. What is the efficiency of the block and tackle?

250.—On a pillar crane equipped with a block and tackle reefed with coil chain, the hook block and the block at the end of the boom each contain two sheaves. Determine the size of the chain required to hoist a load of 60,000 lb. assuming a minimum factor of safety of 3¼ and a value of K as 1.07. What is the efficiency of the block and tackle?

CHAIN TRANSMISSION 49

251.—In a jib crane the hoisting of the load is done by means of a $\frac{5}{8}$-in. coil chain arranged as shown in Fig. 36. Determine the load in the part of the chain leading onto the drum, also the load in the part that is anchored, and the factor of safety used in selecting the chain, having given the following data: (*a*) Magnitude of load Q is 10 tons. (*b*) The diameter of the sheaves is 14 in. and the diameter of the sheave pins is $2\frac{5}{8}$ in. (*c*) The coefficients of chain and journal friction are 0.15 and 0.06 respectively. Determine the overall efficiency from the drum to the hook.

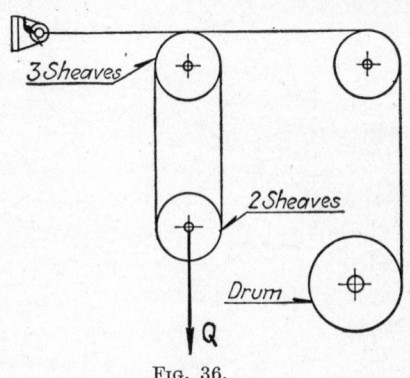

FIG. 36.

252.—A 10-ton pillar crane is equipped with a block and tackle reefed with coil chain arranged so that both the hook block and that at the end of the boom contain two sheaves. Determine the size of the chain required to hoist the full load, assuming a minimum factor of safety of five and a value of K as 1.06. What is the efficiency of the block and tackle?

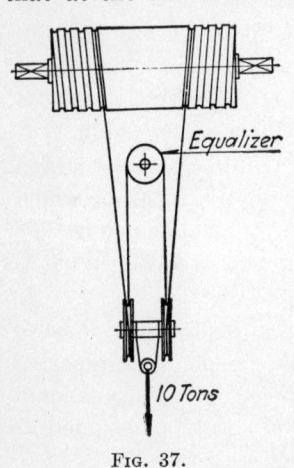

253.—A 60-ton electric traveling crane is equipped with a 10-ton auxiliary hoisting drum reefed with a $\frac{9}{16}$-in. chain arranged as shown in Fig. 37. Determine the maximum load coming on the chain and the factor of safety used in selecting the chain, having given the following data: (*a*) The diameter of the sheaves is 17 in. and the diameter of the sheave pins

FIG. 37.

is $2\frac{1}{2}$ in. (*b*) The coefficients of chain and journal friction are 0.15 and 0.06 respectively. Also determine the efficiency from the drum to the hook.

254.—The main hoisting drums and blocks of a 30-ton electric traveling crane are arranged as shown in Fig. 38. Determine the maximum load coming on the chain and the factor of safety

4

used in selecting the chain, having given the following data: (*a*) The diameter of the sheaves is 21 in. and the diameter of the sheave pins is $3\frac{1}{4}$ in. (*b*) The coefficients of chain and journal friction are 0.12 and 0.06 respectively. Also determine the efficiency from the drum to the hook.

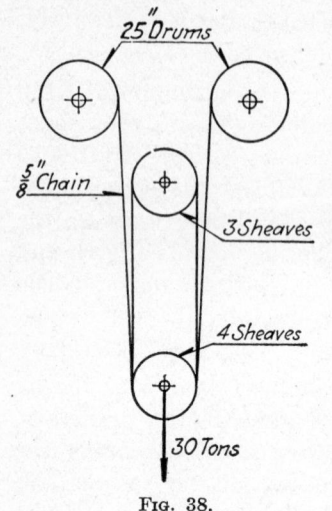

255.—In a differential chain block a pull of 216 lb. is required to raise a load of 2,000 lb., and in order to raise this load through a distance of 1 ft., it is necessary to over-haul 30 ft. of chain. Determine the probable values of K and n.

256.—In a differential chain block a pull of 308 lb. is required to raise a load of 4,000 lb., and in order to raise this load through a distance of 1 ft., it is necessary to over-haul 42 ft. of chain. Determine the probable values of K and n.

FIG. 38.

257.—In a jib crane, having a capacity of 30 tons, the hoisting is done by means of a 1-in. coil chain arranged as shown in Fig. 39.

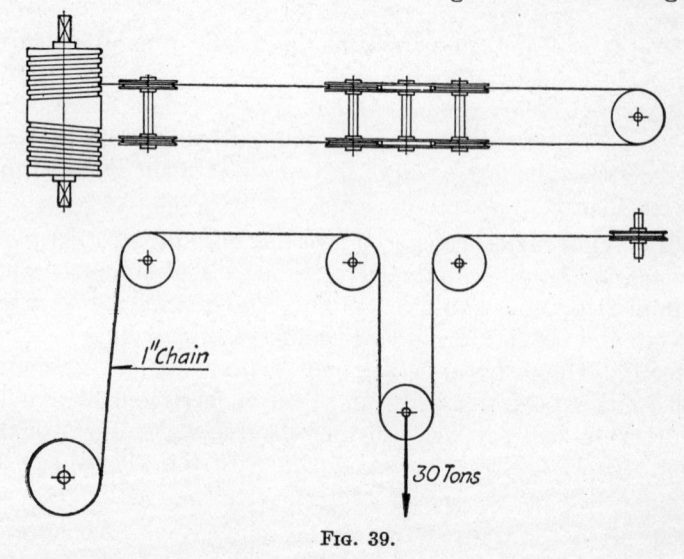

FIG. 39.

CHAIN TRANSMISSION

Having given the following data, determine the load in the part of the chain leading onto the drum, and the factor of safety used in selecting the chain: (a) The diameter of the sheaves is 17 in. and the diameter of the sheave pins is $2^{13}/_{16}$ in. (b) The coefficients of chain and journal friction are 0.12 and 0.06 respectively. Also determine the efficiency from the drum to the hook.

258.—In a brick-making plant a 10-hp. motor, running at 1,150 r.p.m., is connected to a bucket elevator by means of a silent chain. The driven sprocket on the elevator driving shaft is to run at 245 r.p.m. approximately. Assuming the sprocket on the motor shaft has 17 teeth and that the distance between the sprockets is 24 in., determine the following: (a) The pitch and width of Morse chain required for the installation. (b) The pitch and width of Link Belt chain required for the installation. (c) Length of each of the above chains.

259.—A ventilating fan, operating at 190 r.p.m., is driven by means of Link Belt silent chain from a 20-hp. motor, running at 900 r.p.m. Having given the following data, determine the pitch, width and length of chain required for this installation, assuming the speed of the chain is to be kept between 1,000 and 1,300 ft. per minute. (a) The number of teeth on the motor sprocket is 19. (b) The distance between the shafts is 30 in.

260.—It is required to transmit, by means of a Morse silent chain, 150 hp. from a motor running at 435 r.p.m. to a drive shaft running at 85 r.p.m. Assuming that the motor sprocket has 23 teeth and that the distance between the two shafts is 84 in., determine the pitch, width, and length of chain necessary for this installation.

261.—A gas engine, capable of transmitting 85 hp. at 290 r.p.m., is connected to an air compressor by means of a Morse silent chain of 2-in. pitch and 5-in. width. The driving sprocket has 29 teeth and the spring-cushioned sprocket on the compressor has 57 teeth. The distance between the shafts is 68 in. Assuming that the chain transmits the full power of the engine, determine the working load per inch width of chain and the length of the chain. How does this load compare with the allowable load recommended by the manufacturer?

262.—A motor, transmitting 100 hp. at 575 r.p.m., is connected by means of a Link Belt silent chain to a shaft running at 195 r.p.m. Determine the pitch, width and length of chain required for this drive having given the following data: (a) Number of teeth on the motor sprocket is 17. (b) Distance between the shafts is 33 in. (c) The speed of the chain is to be kept between 1,100 and 1,300 ft. per minute. (d) The demand for power may be considered as uniform.

263.—A 25-hp. motor, running at 860 r.p.m., is conected to a rotary blower by means of a silent chain. The motor sprocket has 23 teeth and that on the blower shaft has 65 teeth. The distance between the shafts is 24 in. Determine the following: (a) The pitch, width and length of Link Belt chain required for this installation. (b) The pitch, width and length of Morse chain required for this installation.

264.—A $7\frac{1}{2}$-hp. motor, running at 875 r.p.m., is connnected to the countershaft of a jointer by means of a silent chain. The motor sprocket has 27 teeth and that on the countershaft has 37 teeth. Assuming the distance between the two sprockets as 30 in., determine the pitch, width and length of Morse chain, also of Link Belt chain, required for this installation.

265.—An air compressor, running at approximately 150 r.p.m., is connected to a 75-hp. motor running at 600 r.p.m. by means of a Link Belt silent chain. Determine the pitch, width and length of chain, also the load coming upon the springs of the spring-cushioned sprocket and the length of the springs when transmitting this load, having given the following data: (a) The sprocket on the motor shaft has 19 teeth, and the distance between the shafts is 38 in. (b) The spring-cushioned sprocket has six springs located $6\frac{5}{8}$ in. from the center. (c) Each spring has $6\frac{2}{3}$ coils of $\frac{1}{2}$-in. wire and a free length of $3\frac{1}{2}$ in. (d) The outside diameter of the coils is 2 in. (e) The speed of the chain should be kept between 1,000 and 1,500 ft. per minute. (f) Due to the intermittent load, the size of the chain and the spring load should be based on a rating of 40 to 50 per cent above the normal output of the motor.

266. A 10-hp. motor, running at 800 r.p.m., drives an air compressor at 160 r.p.m. by means of a Link Belt silent chain. The sprocket on the compressor shaft is of the spring-cushioned type. Determine the pitch, width and length of chain required, also the load coming upon the springs of the spring-cushioned sprocket and the length of the springs when transmitting this load, having given the following data: (a) The sprocket on the motor shaft has 17 teeth, and the distance between the shafts is 32 in. (b) The speed of the chain should be kept between 1,000 and 1,300 ft. per minute. (c) The spring-cushioned sprocket has four springs located $5\frac{1}{4}$ in. from the center. (d) Each spring has 6.83 coils of $\frac{3}{8}$-in. wire and a free length of 4 in. (e) The outside diameter of the coils is $2\frac{1}{4}$ in. (f) Due to the non-uniform load the width of the chain and the load upon the springs should be based on an increase of 40 to 50 per cent in the horsepower transmitted by the motor.

267.—A $1\frac{1}{2}$-in. Morse silent chain 10 in. wide is used for transmitting 125 hp. through a spring-cushioned sprocket of the Morse type. Four springs located $11\frac{3}{8}$ in. from the center of the sprocket are used. Each spring has 8.5 coils of $\frac{3}{4}$-in. wire and has an outside diameter of $3\frac{1}{2}$ in. (a) Determine the amount that the springs will be compressed when the chain transmits the full power, assuming the sprocket has 69 teeth and runs at 158 r.p.m. (b) How does the actual load transmitted by the chain compare with the allowable load recommended by the manufacturer?

268.—A 5-hp. motor, running at 1,700 r.p.m., is connected to a textile machine by means of a Morse silent chain of $\frac{5}{8}$-in. pitch and 2 in. wide. The motor sprocket has 17 teeth and that on the machine has 45. The distance between the two shafts is 15 in. Determine the actual load per inch width of chain and the ratio that this load bears to the allowable load recommended by the manufacturer. What is the length of the chain?

269.—At the Ox-Bow hydro-electric plant of the Idaho-Oregon Light and Power Co., two 48-in. water wheels are connected to a 3,600-kw. alternator by means of eight 2-in. Morse silent chains, each of which is 21 in. wide. The water-wheel shafts make 149 r.p.m. and the alternator runs at 225 r.p.m. The driving sprockets on the water-wheel shafts contain 71 teeth, and the distance between the alternator shaft and each water-wheel shaft is 10.75 ft. Determine the following: (a) The number of teeth in the driven sprockets. (b) The length of each chain. (c) The actual tension per inch width of chain and the ratio it bears to the allowable tension recommended by the manufacturer.

270.—A 25-hp. motor, running at 725 r.p.m., is connected to a triplex pump by means of a silent chain. The sprocket on the motor shaft has 17 teeth and that on the pump shaft has 59 teeth. Having given the minimum distance between the shafts as 29.75 in., determine the following: (*a*) The pitch, width and length of the Link Belt silent chain required for this installation. (*b*) The pitch, width and length of the Morse chain required for this installation.

271.—A 50-hp. motor, running at 865 r.p.m., is connected to a triplex pump by means of a 1.2- by 5.5-in. Morse chain. The sprocket on the motor shaft has 17 teeth and that on the pump shaft has 57 teeth. Having given the minimum distance between the shafts as 30 in., determine the following: (*a*) The actual load per inch width of chain and the ratio it bears to the allowable load recommended by the manufacturer. (*b*) The length of the chain.

272.—A line shaft receives power from a 50-hp. motor, running at 850 r.p.m., through a 1.2- by 7-in. Morse chain. The sprocket on the motor shaft has 17 teeth and that on the line shaft has 73 teeth. Having given the minimum distance between the shafts as 49.5 in., determine the following: (*a*) The actual load per inch width of chain and the ratio it bears to the allowable load recommended by the manufacturer. (*b*) The length of the chain.

273.—A 30-hp. motor, running at 860 r.p.m., is connected to a line shaft by means of a silent chain. The sprocket on the motor shaft has 21 teeth and that on the line shaft has 62 teeth. If the minimum distance between the shafts is 60 in., determine the following: The pitch, width and length of Morse chain required for this installation. (*b*) The pitch, width and length of Link Belt chain required for this installation.

274.—Determine the pitch, width and length of a Diamond roller chain required to transmit 3 hp. from a motor to a countershaft. The distance between the shafts is approximately 24 in., and the speeds of the motor and the countershaft are 1,150 and 330 r.p.m. respectively. The maximum diameter of the sprocket on the countershaft is limited to 16 in.

275.—It is desired to transmit 10 hp. from a motor, running at 1,150 r.p.m., to a line shaft running at 360 r.p.m. by means of a roller chain. If the distance between the shafts is approximately 40 in. and the maximum diameter of the sprocket on the line shaft is limited to 18 in., determine the pitch, width and length of Diamond roller chain required for this transmission.

CHAIN TRANSMISSION

276.—A roller chain is to transmit 15 hp. from a motor, running at 885 r.p.m., to a shaft running at 350 r.p.m. If the distance between the shafts is approximately 45 in. and the maximum diameter of the sprocket on the driven shaft is limited to 20 in., determine the pitch, width and length of Diamond roller chain required for this transmission.

277.—Determine the pitch, width and length of Diamond roller chain required to transmit 12 hp. from a countershaft to a conveyor head-shaft. The distance between the shafts is approximately 60 in. and the speeds of the driving and driven shafts are 420 and 175 r.p.m. respectively.

278.—A roller chain is used to transmit 8 hp. from a line shaft to a countershaft. The distance between the shafts is approximately 54 in. and the maximum diameter of the driven sprocket is limited to 18 in. If the revolutions per minute of the driving and driven shafts are 480 and 175 respectively, determine the pitch, width and length of Diamond roller chain required for this transmission.

SECTION IX

FRICTION TRANSMISSION

279.—It is desired to transmit 10 hp. by means of a spur friction transmission. The 8-in. driver is faced with tarred fiber and makes 420 r.p.m. (a) If the follower is made of cast iron, determine the least thrusts on the shafts and the face of the friction wheels. (b) If leather fiber is substituted for the tarred fiber, determine the least thrusts on the shaft and the face of the wheels.

280.—It is required to transmit 20 hp. by means of a spur friction transmission. The 12-in. driver, faced with leather fiber, makes 360 r.p.m. (a) Assuming the follower to be made of cast iron, determine the least thrusts on the shafts and the face of the friction wheels. (b) If tarred fiber is substituted for the leather fiber, determine the least thrusts on the shafts and the face of the wheels.

281 to 284.—For a spur friction driven drum hoist similar to that shown in Fig. 40 and having the dimensions given in Table 11, it is required to determine the following: (a) The factor of safety used in selecting the size of 6 by 19 plow-steel rope, assuming a 24-in. guide sheave is interposed between the load and the drum. (b) The total radial pressure that must be provided between the friction wheels in order to raise the load, and compare the actual working pressure with the allowable pressure given in the Text, assuming the pinion is made of tarred fiber and the driven wheel of cast iron. (c) The size of the belt required to operate the hoist, assuming rawhide laced joints and that the angle of contact is 180 deg. (d) The bearing pressure coming upon each of the bearings, assuming the rope leads from the drum vertically upwards to a head sheave, and that the driving belt runs horizontally to the right. The two shafts may be assumed to lie in the same horizontal plane. (e) The magnitude of the stress in the driving shaft.

TABLE 11

Problem number	Load on rope	Rope		Drum		Drum shaft diameter	Bearings					
							A		*B*		*C* and *D*	
		Size, inches	Speed	Diameter	Length		Diameter	Length	Diameter	Length	Diameter	Length
281	1,300	3/8	150	12	24	2 15/16	2 15/16	10 1/2	2 15/16	10 1/2	2 7/16	7 1/2
282	2,000	9/16	300	20	24	3 15/16	3 15/16	13	3 15/16	14	2 15/16	9
283	3,000	5/8	300	24	30	4 7/16	4 7/16	14	4 7/16	15 3/4	3 7/16	10 1/2

Problem number	Spur frictions				Drive shaft diameter	Pulley		Dimensions				
	Driver		Driven									
	Diameter	Face	Diameter	Face		Diameter	Face	*a*	*b*	*c*	*d*	*e*
281	10	7	40	6	2 7/16	30	6	8 3/4	7 3/4	44 1/2	18 3/4	2 3/8
282	12	9	54	8	2 15/16	36	8	11	9 1/2	49 1/2	20 1/2	2 15/16
283	12	12	72	11	3 7/16	36	10	12 1/2	11	58	24 3/8	2 11/16

284.—In a Billings and Spencer friction-board drop hammer, the driving rolls are 11 in. in diameter and the board attached to the 1,000-lb. ram has a face of 10 in. The 32-in. driving pulleys, running at 130 r.p.m., receive power from two belts each of which is 7 in. wide and 3/8 in. thick. The maximum height of ram travel is 57 in. Assuming that the ratio of T and Q is 1.8, determine the following: (*a*) The number of seconds required to raise the ram through its maximum travel. (*b*) The time required by the ram to fall through the maximum travel. (*c*) The work lost due to slippage. (*d*) The horsepower required to operate the hammer, assuming 2 sec. are lost during each cycle.

285.—In a Billings and Spencer friction-board drop hammer, the driving rolls are 9 in. in diameter and the board attached to the 600-lb. ram has a face of 8 in. The 30-in. driving pulleys, running at 170 r.p.m., are driven by two belts each of which is 6 in. wide and 3/8 in. thick. The ram has a maximum travel of 48 in. Assuming that the ratio of T to Q is 1.75, determine the following: (*a*) The number of seconds required to raise the ram through its maximum travel. (*b*) The time required by the ram to fall through the maximum travel. (*c*) The work lost due to slippage. (*d*) The horsepower required to operate the hammer, assuming 2 sec. are lost during each cycle.

286.—In a Billings and Spencer friction-board drop hammer, the driving rolls are 13 in. in diameter and the board attached to

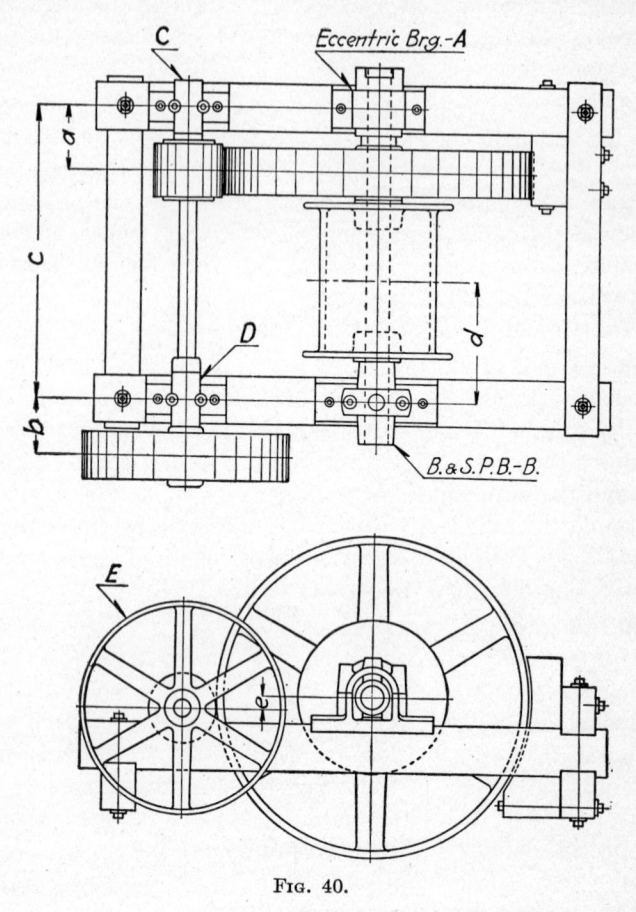

Fig. 40.

the 1600-lb. ram has a face of 10 in. The 42-in. driving pulleys, running at 110 r.p.m., receive power from two belts each of which is 7 in. wide and ⅜ in. thick. The maximum height of ram travel is 54 in. Assuming that the ratio of T to Q is 1.75, determine the following: (*a*) The number of seconds required to raise the ram through its maximum travel. (*b*) The time required by the ram to fall through the maximum travel. (*c*) The work lost due to slippage. (*d*) The horsepower required to operate the hammer, assuming 2 sec. are lost during each cycle.

287.—It is desired to transmit 24 hp. by means of a pair of grooved-spur friction wheels, the driven wheel being 18 in. in diameter and running at 320 r.p.m. Assuming the angle of the grooves as 45 deg. and the coefficient of friction as 0.2, determine the pressure between the wheels.

288.—A pair of cast-iron grooved-spur friction wheels is used for transmitting 12 hp. between two shafts located 25 in. apart. The driving shaft makes 200 r.p.m. and the driven shaft 50 r.p.m. Assuming the groove angle as 40 deg., the coefficient of friction as 0.15 and the permissible pressure per inch of contact as 400 lb., determine the following: (*a*) The radial pressure upon the two wheels. (*b*) The number of grooves required, assuming the effective depth t of the grooves as $\frac{1}{2}$ in.

289.—A pair of cast-iron grooved spur friction wheels is used for transmitting 18 hp. between two shafts located 30 in. apart. The driving shaft makes 260 r.p.m. and the driven shaft 65 r.p.m. Assuming the groove angle as 40 deg., the coefficient of friction as 0.16 and the permissible pressure per inch of contact as 400 lb., determine the following: (*a*) The radial pressure upon the two wheels. (*b*) The number of grooves required, assuming the effective depth t of the grooves as $\frac{5}{8}$ in.

290.—A pair of cast-iron grooved-spur friction wheels is used for transmitting 8 hp. between two shafts 20 in. apart. The driving shaft makes 360 r.p.m. and the driven shaft 90 r.p.m. Assuming the angle of the grooves as 40 deg., the coefficient of friction as 0.16 and the permissible pressure per inch of contact as 400 lb., determine the following: (*a*) The radial pressure upon the two wheels. (*b*) The number of grooves required assuming the effective depth t of the grooves as $\frac{1}{2}$ in.

291.—Two bevel friction wheels, having a velocity ratio of 5 to 2, transmit 10 hp. The 10-in. driver having a 4-in. face is made of straw fiber and runs at 600 r.p.m., determine the following, assuming the driven wheel is made of cast iron: (*a*) The axial thrust coming upon each shaft for both the starting and the running condition. (*b*) The maximum normal pressure per inch of face.

292.—A bevel friction transmission, having a velocity ratio of 3 to 1, transmits 8 hp. at 500 r.p.m. of the straw-fiber driving wheel.

The cast-iron driven wheel is 24 in. in diameter and has a face of 4 in., determine the following: (a) The axial thrust coming upon each shaft for both the starting and the running condition. (b) The maximum normal pressure per inch of face.

293.—A pair of 18-in. bevel friction wheels is used for transmitting 10 hp. at 360 r.p.m. of the leather-fiber driving wheel. Determine the required face of the wheels and the maximum axial thrust coming upon each shaft, assuming the driven wheel is made of cast iron.

294.—Two 16-in. bevel friction wheels are used for transmitting 6 hp. at 400 r.p.m. of the straw-fiber driving wheel. Determine the required face of the wheels and the maximum axial thrust coming upon each shaft, assuming the driven wheel is made of cast iron.

295.—A bevel friction transmission, having a velocity ratio of 2 to 1, transmits 6 hp. at 400 r.p.m. of the tarred-fiber driving wheel. The cast-iron driven wheel is 16 in. in diameter and has a face of 5 in., determine the following: (a) The axial thrust coming upon each shaft for both the starting and the running condition. (b) The maximum normal pressure per inch of face.

296.—What horsepower may be transmitted by a pair of 12-in. bevel friction wheels having a 4-in. face and running at 380 r.p.m.? One of the wheels is made of tarred fiber and the other of cast iron. What axial thrust comes upon each wheel during the running condition?

297.—A 12-in. friction bevel wheel, made of tarred fiber and having a 4-in. face, is used with an 18-in. cast-iron wheel. If the 12-in. driver makes 300 r.p.m., what horsepower may be transmitted? What axial thrust comes upon each of the wheels during the running condition?

298.—A 10-in. friction bevel wheel, made of leather fiber and having a 4-in. face, is used with a 20-in. cast-iron wheel. If the 10-in. driver makes 320 r.p.m., what horsepower may be transmitted? What axial thrust comes upon each of the wheels during the running condition?

299.—A crown friction transmisson, similar to the one shown in Fig. 41, has a cast-iron disk having an outside diameter of $18\frac{7}{8}$ in. The crown wheel, made of leather fiber, has a face of $1\frac{3}{8}$ in. and a diameter of 21 in. The shaft e is $1\frac{7}{8}$ in. in diameter and the dimensions q and s are 6⅝ in. and 28¼ in. respectively. The chain sprocket f is about 3¼ in. in diameter. Assuming that the coefficient of friction for sliding between wheel c and shaft e is 0.06, determine the following for both the maximum and the minimum speeds: (a) The horsepower that may be transmitted from the disk b to the crown wheel c, assuming the shaft a makes 1,500 r.p.m. and that the minimum and the maximum

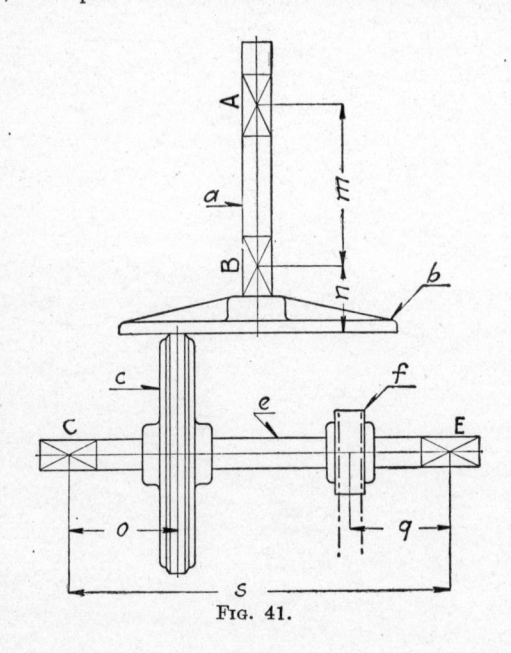

Fig. 41.

value of the dimension o are 5¾ in. and 12⅛ in. respectively. (b) The tangential force on the sprocket f and the size of the roller chain required for the maximum force. (c) The maximum reactions coming upon the bearings C and E, and the size of Hyatt roller bearings required at C and E. Using ball bearings, what sizes are required? (d) The maximum stress in the shaft e.

300.—A crown friction transmission, similar to the one shown in Fig. 41, has a cast-iron disk having an outside diameter of 21½ in. The crown wheel made of leather fiber has a face of 1½ in. and a diameter of 20 in. The shaft e is 1⅞ in. in diameter and the dimensions q and s are 3⅝ in. and 24½ in. respectively. The chain sprocket f is approximately 3¾ in. in diameter. Assuming that the coefficient of friction for sliding between the wheel *c* and the shaft *e* is 0.06, determine the following for both the maximum and the minimum speeds: (*a*) The horsepower that may be transmitted from the disk *b* to the crown wheel *c*, assuming the shaft *a* makes 1,000 r.p.m. and that the minimum and maximum value of the dimension *o* are $2\frac{1}{4}$ in. and 10 in. respectively. (*b*) The tangential force on the sprocket *f* and the size of the roller chain required for the maximum force. (*c*) The maximum reactions coming upon the bearings *C* and *E*, and the size of Hyatt roller bearings required at *C* and *E*. Using ball bearings, what sizes are required? (*d*) The maximum stress in the shaft *e*.

SECTION X

SPUR GEARING

301.—A train of cast spur gears transmits 10 hp. at 250 r.p.m. of the cast-iron pinion. If the pitch diameter of the pinion is approximately 6 in., and the velocity ratio is approximately 4.5 to 1, determine the following, assuming 15-deg. involute teeth: (a) The circular pitch and face. (b) The number of teeth in the pinion and gear, also the correct pitch diameters of the pinion and gear. (c) Make a full sized layout of the pinion tooth, giving all necessary dimensions. (d) The dimensions of the arm of the gear, assuming an elliptical cross-section is used.

302.—A train of cast spur gears transmits 18 hp. at 50 r.p.m. of the cast-iron gear. If the pitch diameter of the cast-iron driving pinion is approximately 8 in., and the velocity ratio is approximately 3.5 to 1, determine the following, assuming 15-deg. fovolute teeth: (a) The circular pitch and face. (b) The number of teeth in the pinion and gear, also the correct pitch diameters of the pinion and gear. (c) Make a full sized layout in the pinion tooth giving all necessary dimensions. (d) The dimensions of the arm of the gear, assuming an elliptical cross-section.

303.—A train of cast spur gears transmits 15 hp. at 60 r.p.m. of the cast-iron gear. If the pitch diameter of the cast-iron driving pinion is approximately 8 in., and the velocity ratio is approximately 4 to 1, determine the following, assuming 15-deg. involute teeth: (a) The circular pitch and face. (b) The number of teeth in the pinion and gear, also the correct pitch diameters of the pinion and gear. (c) The dimensions of the arm of the gear, assuming an elliptical cross-section. (d) Make a full sized layout of the pinion tooth, giving all necessary dimensions.

304.—A train of cast spur gears transmits 25 hp. at 225 r.p.m. of the cast-iron pinion. If the pitch diameter of the pinion is approximately 10 in., and the velocity ratio is approximately 3 to 1, determine the following, assuming 15-deg. involute teeth: (a) The circular pitch and face. (b) The number of teeth in the pinion and gear, also the correct pitch diameters of the pinion and gear. (c) Make a full sized layout of the pinion tooth giving all necessary dimensions. (d) The dimensions of the arm of the gear, assuming an elliptical cross-section is used.

305.—A machine cut Fabroil spur pinion used for driving a large pump, transmits 225 hp. at 84 r.p.m. It has 74 teeth of 1¼-in. pitch and its face is 18 in. Determine the diameter of the pinion and the probable fiber stress in the teeth, assuming the latter to be 14.5-deg. involute.

306.—A machine cut cast-iron spur gear having 192 teeth of 6-in. pitch and a 30-in. face, runs at 10 r.p.m. Determine the diameter of, and the horsepower transmitted by this gear, assuming cycloidal teeth.

307.—Determine the magnitude of the stresses in the teeth of a triple-staggered-tooth cut steel gear and pinion transmitting 1,600 hp. at a pitch line speed of 2,000 ft. per minute, having given the following data: Number of teeth in the gear is 154 and in the pinion 20; the circular pitch is 5½ in. and the total length of the gear face is 38 in. What are the diameters of the gears?

308 to 337.—For the particular train of cut spur gears assigned for discussion, use the data given in Table 12 and determine the diametral pitch and face of the gears, assuming first, that 14.5-deg. involute teeth are used and second, that stub teeth are used. In the case of rawhide, Fabroil and Bakelite Micarta-D gears, make a neat dimensioned sketch of the gear.

337.—In a motor car, it is desired to transmit 24 hp. from the high-speed shaft to the intermediate by means of spur gears having Fellows stub teeth. Determine the diametral pitch and face of the gears having given the following data: (a) The diameters of the gear and pinion are 4½ in. and 2½ in. respectively. (b) The face of the gears varies from 1 to 1½ times the circular pitch. (c) The speed of the motor is 1,600. (d) Both gears are made of hardened chrome-nickel steel.

338.—A slip gear similar to the one shown in Fig. 152 of the Text has 76 teeth of 4 pitch and a face of 3 in. The inner and outer diameters of the cast-iron hub b in contact with the gear a are 4 in. and 6 in. respectively. The large and small diameters of the cone c are 6 in. and 5³⁄₁₆ in. respectively, and the angle between the axis and an element of the cone is 15 deg. (a) Determine the axial thrust that the disk spring e must exert in

SPUR GEARING

Table 12

Problem number	Horse-power	Velocity ratio	Pinion Diameter	Pinion Material	Gear Revolutions per minute	Gear Material
308	10	4 to 1	5		280	
309	15	3⅓ to 1	6		210	
310	20	4 to 1	6	Cast iron	200	
311	25	3 to 1	7		275	
312	30	3 to 1	8		240	
313	15	3⅓ to 1	6		210	
314	20	4 to 1	6	Rawhide	200	
315	25	3 to 1	7		275	
316	15	3⅓ to 1	6		210	Cast iron
317	20	4 to 1	6	Fabroil	200	
318	25	3 to 1	7		275	
319	15	3⅓ to 1	6	Bakelite	210	
320	20	4 to 1	6	Micarta-D	200	
321	25	3 to 1	7		275	
322	20	4 to 1	6		200	
323	25	3 to 1	7	Bronze	275	
324	30	3 to 1	8		240	
325	25	3.5 to 1	8	High-grade	200	
326	35	4 to 1	8	cast iron	180	
327	50	4 to 1	8		180	
328	25	3.5 to 1	8	High-grade	200	
329	35	4 to 1	8	bronze	180	Steel casting
330	50	4 to 1	8		180	
331	25	3.5 to 1	6	Machinery	280	
332	35	4 to 1	6	steel	220	
333	50	4 to 1	7		180	
334	25	3.5 to 1	6		280	
335	35	4 to 1	6	Alloy steel	220	
336	50	4 to 1	7		180	

order that the gear may transmit, to the shaft d, the full working load for which the steel-casting gear a was designed. The coefficient of friction for the cone c may be taken as 0.08 and that for the flanged hub b as 0.06. (b) What is the normal pressure per square inch of cone surface? (c) Determine the tensile stress induced in the shaft by the action of the spring e, assuming the threaded shank is 1¾ in. in diameter and that it has eight threads per inch.

339.—In the transmission of a 6-ton truck a spur pinion, having 16 teeth and running at 790 r.p.m., drives a gear having 44 teeth. Determine the horsepower that may be transmitted having given the following data: (a) The diametral pitch and face of the gears are 5 in. and 1½ in., respectively. (b) The teeth are standard 20-deg. involute. (c) Both gears are made of hardened chrome-nickel steel.

340.—In a motor car, low speed is obtained by a train of four spur gears located in the transmission. Assuming the following data, determine the probable stress in the teeth of the various gears and compare these stresses with the permissible stresses derived from the data and formulas given in the Text. (a) Each of the pinions has 18 teeth of ⅝ pitch, and each gear has 33 teeth. (b) The face of all of the gears is ⅞ in., and all gears are made of hardened chrome-vanadium steel. (c) The motor is capable of delivering 40 hp. at 1,800 r.p.m.

341.—In a motor car, low speed is obtained by a train of four gears located in the transmission. Assuming the following data, determine the probable stress in the teeth of the various gears and compare these stresses with those obtained from the data and formulas given in the Text: (a) The pinion on the high-speed shaft has 16 teeth and that on the intermediate shaft has 17 teeth. (b) The gear meshing with the high-speed pinion has 29 teeth, and that gearing with the intermediate pinion has 28 teeth. (c) The diametral pitch and face of the gears are 5 and 1 in. respectively, and the teeth are standard 20-deg. involute. (d) All gears are made of hardened chrome-nickel steel. (e) The motor is capable of delivering 60 hp. at 1,800 r.p.m.

342.—(a) Determine the axial thrust that must be applied to the bronze cones b and c of the slip gear shown in Fig. 153 of the Text, so that the full working load for which the forged-steel pinion d was designed, may be transmitted. Assume the following data: The pinion has 30 teeth of 5 pitch and a face of 2 in.; the large diameter of the conical bore is $4\frac{1}{4}$ in. and the face of each cone is $1\frac{5}{8}$ in.; the angle between the axis and an element of the cone is 7 deg.; the coefficient of friction is 0.08. (b) Determine the amount that the spring e must be compressed in order to produce the desired axial thrust, having given the following data: The spring has an outside diameter of $3\frac{5}{8}$ in. and contains seven coils of $\frac{3}{8}$ in. steel wire.

343.—A spring-cushioned gear, similar to the one shown in Fig. 154 of the Text, has 68 teeth of $2\frac{1}{2}$ pitch. The gear has a $5\frac{1}{4}$ in. face and the rim is a steel forging. Assuming the teeth to be 14.5-deg. involute, determine the horsepower that may be transmitted at 200 r.p.m. (b) If seven springs located at $9\frac{3}{4}$ in. from the center of the gear are used, determine the free length of the spring assuming each spring has 7.5 coils of $\frac{1}{2}$-in. steel wire, the outer diameter of the coils being $2\frac{1}{4}$ in. The springs, in place in the gear, have a length of $3\frac{31}{32}$ in.

344.—A $7\frac{1}{2}$-hp. motor, running at 670 r.p.m., is connected to a punching and shearing machine by means of spur gears. The motor pinion is made of Bakelite Micarta-D and has 32 teeth of 4 pitch. The face of the pinion is $3\frac{1}{2}$ in. The driven gear is made of a good grade of cast iron. Assuming standard 14.5-deg. involute teeth, determine the probable stress in the teeth and compare the result with that obtained from the data and formula given in the Text.

SECTION XI

BEVEL AND SCREW GEARING

345.—In a machine-moulded bevel-gear train, having a velocity ratio of 2 to 1, the pinion runs at 175 r.p.m. and has 25 teeth of 1½-in. pitch and a face of 4 in. If both gears are made of a good cast iron and the teeth are of the 15-deg. involute type, determine the following: (a) The horsepower that may be transmitted. (b) The resultant tooth pressure and the radius at which this pressure acts on both gears. (c) The magnitude of the thrusts along the shafts. (d) The large outside diameters of the gear and pinion. (e) The face, center and edge angles of the gear and pinion.

346.—In a machine-moulded bevel-gear train, having a velocity ratio of 10 to 3, the pinion makes 180 r.p.m. and has 24 teeth of 1¾-in. pitch and a face of 5 in. Assuming that both gears are made of a good cast iron and that the teeth are of the 15-deg. involute type, determine the following: (a) The horsepower that may be transmitted. (b) The resultant tooth pressure and the radius at which this pressure acts on both gears. (c) The magnitude of the thrusts along the shafts. (d) The large outside diameters of both gears. (e) The face, center and edge angles of both gears.

347.—In a machine-moulded bevel-gear train, having a velocity ratio of 4 to 3, the pinion makes 160 r.p.m. and has 36 teeth of 2-in. pitch and a face of 6½ in. Assuming that both gears are made of the best grade of cast iron and that the teeth are of the 15-deg. involute type, determine the following: (a) The horsepower that may be transmitted. (b) The resultant tooth pressure and the radius at which this pressure acts on both gears. (c) The magnitude of the thrusts along the shafts. (d) The larg outside diameters of both gears. (e) The face, center and edge angles of both gears.

348 to 353.—Using the data given in Table 13 for the particular train of cast bevel gears assigned for discussion, determine the following: (a) The circular pitch and face of the gears. (b) The resultant tooth pressure and the radius at which the pressure acts on both gears. (c) The magnitude of the thrusts along the shafts. (d) The face, center and edge angles of both gears.

TABLE 13

Problem number	Horse-power	Velocity ratio	Pinion Diameter, inches	Pinion Revolutions per minute	Material Pinion	Material Gear	Type of teeth
348	5	1 to 1	8	225	High-grade cast iron		15-deg. involute
349	8	2 to 1	9	250			15-deg. involute
350	10	3 to 2	8	240	Good cast iron		15-deg. involute
351	15	2 to 1	6	420	High-grade cast iron		20-deg. involute
352	20	3 to 1	8	300	High-grade cast iron		15-deg. involute

353.—A bevel-gear drive on the rear axle of a motor car consists of a case-hardened alloy-steel gear having 48 teeth of 1¼-in. face and a pinion, made of hardened chrome-vanadium steel, having 15 teeth of 5 pitch. If the teeth are the standard 20-deg. involute type and that 25 hp. is transmitted at 1,800 r.p.m. of the pinion, determine the following: (a) The probable stress in both gears and compare these stresses with those obtained from the formula given in the Text. (b) The resultant tooth pressure and the radius at which this pressure acts on both gears. (c) The magnitude of the thrusts along the shafts.

354.—In a motor car, the bevel-gear drive on the rear axle consists of a case-hardened alloy-steel gear having 52 teeth, and a pinion made of hardened chrome-nickel steel having 13 teeth of 5 pitch and a face of 1¼ in. Assuming the teeth to be of the standard 20-deg. involute type, and that 30 hp. is transmitted at 1,500 r.p.m. of the pinion, determine the following: (a) The probable stress in both gears and compare these stresses with those obtained from the formula given in the Text. (b) The resultant tooth pressure and the radius at which this pressure acts on both gears. (c) The magnitude of the thrusts along the shafts.

355.—In a 3-ton truck the bevel-gear drive, used on the jack shaft, consists of a case-hardened alloy-steel gear having 56 teeth of 4 pitch, and a pinion made of hardened chrome-nickel steel having 13 teeth of 1⅝-in. face. Assuming the teeth to be of the standard 20-deg. involute type, determine the following: (a) The horsepower transmitted by the drive at 1,000 r.p.m. of the pinion shaft. (b) The resultant tooth pressure and the radius at which this pressure acts on both gears. (c) The magnitude of the thrusts along the shafts.

356.—In a 6-ton truck the bevel-gear drive, used on the jack shaft, consists of a case-hardened alloy-steel gear having 57 teeth of 4 pitch, and a pinion made of hardened chrome-vanadium steel having 19 teeth of 2-in. face. Assuming the teeth as standard 20-deg. involute, determine the following: (a) The horsepower that may be transmitted by the drive at 900 r.p.m. of the pinion shaft. (b) The resultant tooth pressure and the radius at which this pressure acts on both gears. (c) The magnitude of the thrusts along the shafts.

357.—The bevel-gear drive on the rear axle of a motor car consists of a case-hardened alloy-steel gear having 53 teeth of 5.5 pitch, and a pinion made of hardened chrome-vanadium steel having 13 teeth and a face of 1 3/16 in. Assuming the teeth to be of the standard 20-deg. involute type and that 20 hp. is transmitted at 1,800 r.p.m. of the pinion, determine the following: (a) The probable stress in both gears and compare these stresses with those obtained from the formula given in the Text. (b) The resultant tooth pressure and the radius at which this pressure acts on both gears. (c) The magnitude of the thrusts along the shafts.

358.—A train of cut bevel gears transmits 40 hp. at 1,000 r.p.m. of the pinion. If the pitch diameter of the gear is limited to a maximum of 11 in., and the velocity ratio is 4 to 1, determine the following, assuming stub teeth are used: (a) The pitch and face of the gears. (b) The number of teeth in each gear, also the large pitch diameters. (c) The resultant tooth pressure and the radius at which this pressure acts on both gears. (d) The magnitude of the thrusts along the shafts. (e) The face, center and edge angles of both gears. (NOTE.—The pinion is to be made of hardened chrome-nickel steel and the gear of case-hardened alloy steel.)

359.—A train of cut bevel gears transmits 25 hp. at 500 r.p.m. of the pinion. If the pitch diameter of the gear is limited to a maximum of 11 in. and the velocity ratio is 3.5 to 1, determine the following, assuming stub teeth are used and that the pinion is made of hardened chrome-vanadium steel and the gear of case-hardened alloy steel: (a) The pitch and face of the gears. (b) The number of teeth in each gear and the large pitch diameters. (c) The resultant tooth pressure and the radius at which this pressure acts on both gears. (d) The magnitude of the thrusts along the shafts. (e) The face, center and edge angles of both gears.

360 to 366.—Using the data given in Table 14 for the particular train of cut bevel gears assigned for discussion, determine the following: (a) The diametral pitch and face of the gears. (b) The resultant tooth pressure and the radius at which the pressure acts on both gears. (c) The magnitude of the thrusts along the shafts. (d) The face, center and edge angles of both gears.

TABLE 14

Problem number	Horse-power	Velocity ratio	Pinion Diameter, inches	Pinion Revolutions per minute	Material Pinion	Material Gear	Type of teeth
360	10	1 to 1	8	400	High-grade cast iron		Stub
361	15	5 to 3	6	375	H. G. Br.	H. G. C. I.	
362	20	5 to 2	7	350	Bronze	H. G. C. I.	
363	20	1 to 1	20	180	Good cast iron		14.5-deg. involute
364	25	3 to 2	8	360	Mch. St.	St. Ctg.	
365	30	2 to 1	8	360	H. G. Br.	H. G. C. I.	Stub

366.—Determine the magnitude of the stresses in the teeth of a double helical gear used for transmitting 1,800 hp. at 54 r.p.m. to a rolling mill. This gear, shown in detail in Fig. 177 of the Text, contains 101 teeth of one diametral pitch. The teeth are of the

20-deg. involute type having a helix angle of 23 deg., and the material used in the construction of the gear is steel casting. The drive is encased and it may be assumed that the gears are provided with scanty lubrication and that they are inspected frequently. Use both Bates' and Day's formulas.

367.—The double helical gear shown in detail in Fig. 184 of the Text is used for driving a duplex mine pump. The gear is made of steel casting and contains 209 teeth of the 20-deg. involute type having a helix angle of 23 deg. Assuming that the gear makes 47 r.p.m., and that the drive is encased and inspected frequently and that the gears are supplied with scanty lubrication, determine the following: (a) The diametral pitch of the gear. (b) The load and horsepower that may be transmitted, using both Bates' and Day's formulas.

368.—A double herring-bone pinion and two large double helical gears, having rims made of steel casting bolted to cast-iron spiders, are used for driving a rail blooming mill. The gear has 116 teeth of the 20-deg. involute type, and the details of the rim are shown in Fig. 179 and 183 of the Text. The details of the pinion, which is made of steel casting, are shown in Fig. 185. Assuming that the gear makes 35 r.p.m. and that the drive is encased and supplied with indifferent lubrication, determine the following: (a) The load and horsepower that may be transmitted by the gear, using both formulas given in the Text. (b) The load and horsepower that may be transmitted by the double pinion, using both formulas. (c) The shearing and bearing stresses in the 4- by 3-in. keys that are used between the rim and the arms of the spider, assuming the coupling bolts are relieved of all shearing action.

369.—The large double helical gear, shown in Figs. 180, 181 and 182 of the Text, is used for driving a sheet mill. The gear has 116 teeth of the $22\frac{1}{2}$-deg. involute type having a helix angle of 30 deg. The rim of the gear is made of steel casting and the spider is made of cast iron. Assuming that the gear makes 32 r.p.m. and that the drive is encased and supplied with indifferent lubrication, determine the following: (a) The load and horse power that may be transmitted by this gear, using both formulas given in the Text. (b) The shearing and bearing stresses in the 4- by 3-in. keys that are used between the rim and the arms of the spider, assuming the coupling bolts are relieved of all shearing action.

370.—A pair of double helical gears are used for reducing the speed of a 75-hp. steam turbine running at 3,000 r.p.m. The 4-in. forged-steel pinion on the turbine shaft drives a steel casting gear located on the shaft of a centrifugal pump running at 600 r.p.m. Assuming that the gears are encased and that a continuous supply of oil is furnished, determine the diametral pitch and the face of the gears, using Bates' formula.

371.—It is desired to transmit power from a 200-hp motor, running at 425 r.p.m., to a rubber mixer running at 85 r.p.m. by means of double helical gearing. The distance between the shafts is approximately 27 in. The driven gear is made of steel casting and the pinion is made integral with the forged steel shaft. Determine the diametral pitch and face of the gears, assuming indifferent lubrication and that the power transmitted varies between fairly wide limits.

372.—A 75-hp. motor, running at 450 r.p.m., is geared to a pump by means of double helical gearing. The forged-steel pinion on the motor shaft is 8 in. in diameter and drives the castiron gear on the pump shaft at 120 r.p.m. Determine the diametral pitch and the face assuming that the gears are indifferently lubricated.

373.—A 100-kw. generator, running at 600 r.p.m., is driven by a steam turbine through the medium of double helical gearing. The heat-treated forged-steel pinion, made integral with the shaft, runs at 3,600 r.p.m. The gear consists of a rolled-steel ring shrunk and keyed onto a cast-iron spider. The gear teeth are continuously supplied with lubricant by a series of oil jets. The pinion is supported between two $2\frac{1}{4}$- by $6\frac{3}{4}$-in. bearings and the gear between two $3\frac{1}{2}$- by $7\frac{1}{4}$-in. bearings. (a) If the distance between the shafts is approximately $12\frac{1}{4}$ in., determine the diametral pitch and face of the gears. (b) Determine the torsional stress in each shaft, also the bearing pressure coming upon each bearing.

374.—A 50-hp. steam turbine, running at 3,000 r.p.m., drives a centrifugal pump at 1,000 r.p.m. by means of double helical gearing. The heat-treated forged-steel pinion is made integral with the shaft, while the gear consists of a rolled-steel ring, shrunk and keyed onto a cast-iron spider. (a) Assuming the teeth receive a continuous supply of lubricant and that the distance between the shafts is 6 in., determine the diametral pitch and face of the gears. (b) If the pinion is supported between two 2- by

6-in. bearings and the gear between two 2½-by 6½-in. bearings, what are the bearing pressures upon each bearing, also what torsional stress is produced in each shaft?

375.—The statement of this problem is identical with that of Prob. 374, with the exception that the size of the turbine is 300 hp.; the speed of the pump is 750; the distance between the shafts is 10 in.; the sizes of the pinion and gear-shaft bearings are 3 by 9 in. and 4 by 9½ in. respectively.

376.—A 45-hp. motor running at 210 to 380 r.p.m. drives a traction elevator by means of double helical gearing having a 7 to 1 velocity ratio. The heat-treated forged-steel pinion is made integral with the shaft, while the 36-in. gear consists of a solid steel casting rim securely bolted to a cast-iron spider. Assuming the teeth receive a continuous supply of lubricant, determine the diametral pitch and face of the gears.

377.—The motor of a truck is capable of developing 36 hp. at 1,000 r.p.m., but only 90 per cent. of this power is actually transmitted to the worm of the worm-gear drive on the rear axle. The speed reduction in the transmission of the truck is 3.36 to 1, and that in the worm and gear is 13 to 1. The worm has a triple thread of 3.75-in. lead and its pitch diameter is 2.5 in. Having given the pressure angle of the worm thread as 30 deg. and the coefficient of friction for the worm and gear as 0.02, determine the following: (*a*) The magnitude of the forces N, P, W and S. (*b*) The efficiency of the worm and gear. (*c*) The magnitude of the loads coming upon the worm-shaft bearings, assuming the distance between the bearings is 12.93 in. (*d*) The magnitude of the loads coming upon the worm gear shaft bearings, assuming the latter are 9.758 in. apart. (*e*) The heat generated in B.t.u. per minute at the surface in contact.

378.—The motor of a truck is capable of developing 39 hp. at 1,000 r.p.m., but only 90 per cent. of this power is available at the worm shaft of the worm-gear drive on the rear axle. The speed reduction in the transmission of the truck is 3.36 to 1, and that in the worm and gear is 11.75 to 1. The worm has a quadruple thread of 4.18-in. lead and its pitch diameter is 2.677 in. Having given the pressure angle of the worm thread as 30 deg. and the coefficient of friction for the worm and gear as 0.02, determine the following: (*a*) The magnitude of the forces N, P, W and S. (*b*) The efficiency of the worm and gear. (*c*) The magnitude of the loads coming upon the worm-shaft bearings, assuming the distance between the bearings is 12.93 in. (d) The magnitude of the loads coming upon the worm-gear shaft bearings, assuming the latter are 9.758 in. apart. (e) The heat generated in B.t.u. per minute at the surface in contact.

379.—The motor of a truck is capable of developing 52 hp. at 1,000 r.p.m., but only 90 per cent. of this power is available at the worm shaft of the worm-gear drive on the rear axle. The speed reduction in the transmission of the truck is 3.36 to 1, and that in the worm and gear is 8.75 to 1. The worm has quadruple thread of 5.5-in. lead and its pitch diameter is 2.88 in. Having given the pressure angle of the worm thread as 30 deg. and the coefficient of friction for the worm and gear as 0.02, determine the following: (a) The magnitude of the forces N, P, W and S. (b) The efficiency of the worm and gear. (c) The magnitude of the loads coming upon the worm-shaft bearings, assuming the distance between the bearings is 12.93 in. (d) The magnitude of the loads coming upon the worm-gear shaft bearings, assuming the latter 9.758 in. apart. (e) The heat generated in B.t.u. per minute at the surface in contact.

380 to 385.—A worm-gear speed-reducer, driven by an electric motor, has a steel worm and a bronze gear. The pressure angle, used on the worm thread, is 14.5 deg. For the particular speed-reducer assigned for discussion, use the data given in Table 15 and determine the following, assuming the coefficient of friction for the worm and gear is 0.04: (a) The magnitude of the forces N, P, W and S. (b) The efficiency of the worm and gear. (c) The magnitude of the loads coming upon the worm-shaft bearings. (d) The magnitude of the loads coming upon the gear-shaft bearings. (e) The torsional stress in the worm shaft. (f) The heat generated in B.t.u. per minute at the surface in contact.

TABLE 15

Problem number	Motor		Worm			Worm gear				Center to center of bearing		Bearing lengths	
	Horsepower	Revolutions per minute	Diameter	Threads	Bore	Teeth	Pitch	Face	Bore	Worm shaft	Gear shaft	Worm shaft	Gear shaft
380	3	1,000	2.042	4	1 5/16	30	3/4	1 7/8	1 7/16	7 11/16	5 3/4	2 1/2	3 3/8
381	5.75	850	3.25	4	1 7/16	36	3 DP	2 3/8	1 15/16	10 3/8	5 15/16	3 1/2	3 1/16
382	9.0	750	3.29	4	1 11/16	42	1 1/4	2 3/4	2 3/16	13 1/8	6 5/8	4 5/8	3 5/8
383	13.5	700	3.59	4	1 11/16	47	1 1/2	3	2 1/16	13 3/8	8 3/8	5	5
384	23.33	650	4.28	4	1 15/16	52	1 3/4	3 3/4	2 15/16	17 1/2	9 1/4	8	5

SECTION XII

COUPLINGS AND CLUTCHES

385.—In a certain installation of a Westinghouse flange coupling having a 1½-in. bore, it is desired that the torsional stress in the shaft shall not exceed 3,500 lb. per square inch. Determine the following, assuming the proportions given in Table 85, page 387 of the Text. (*a*) The horsepower that may be transmitted at 600 r.p.m. (*b*) The shearing and bearing stresses coming upon the bolts. (*c*) The shearing stress in the flanges of the coupling.

386.—The statement of this problem is identical with that of Prob. 385, with the exception that the bore of the coupling is 3 in. and the speed 450.

387.—The statement of this problem is identical with that of Prob. 385, with the exception that the bore of the coupling is 4 in. and the speed 450.

388.—The statement of this problem is identical with that of Prob. 385, with the exception that the bore of the coupling is 6 in. and the speed is 375.

389.—The statement of this problem is identical with that of Prob. 385, with the exception that the bore of the coupling is 8 in. and the speed is 325.

390.—A Bruce-Macbeth leather-link coupling having a bore of 2 3/16 in. transmits 30 hp. at 200 r.p.m. The leather links are 2 in. wide and ⅜ in. thick, and are held in place by six ⅝-in. bolts. Assuming that six of the nine links used are pulling-links, determine the following: (*a*) The torsional stress in the shaft. (*b*) The shearing and bending stresses in the bolts. (*c*) The tensile stress in the leather links.

391.—A Bruce-Macbeth leather-link coupling having a bore of 4 7/16 in. transmits 250 hp. at 250 r.p.m. The leather links are 4 in. wide and ⅜ in. thick, and are held in place by six 1¼-in. bolts. Assuming that 12 of the 18 links used are pulling-links, determine the following: (*a*) The torsional stress in the shaft. (*b*) The shearing and bending stresses in the bolts. (*c*) The tensile stress in the leather links.

COUPLINGS AND CLUTCHES

392.—Determine the number and dimensions of the links, also the size of the bolts required for a leather-link coupling having a $1\frac{11}{16}$-in. bore and the general dimensions given in Table 89, page 394 of the Text, assuming the following permissible stresses: (a) Shearing stress of 4,000 lb. per square inch in the shaft; (b) tensile stress for the leather links, 420 lb. per square inch; (c) bending and shearing stresses in the bolts, 10,500 and 1,450 lb. per square inch respectively.

393.—The statement of this problem is identical with that of Prob. 392, with the exception that the bore of the coupling is $2\frac{3}{16}$ in.

394.—The statement of this problem is identical with that of Prob. 392, with the exception that the bore of the coupling is $3\frac{7}{16}$ in.

395.—The statement of this problem is identical with that of Prob. 392, with the exception that the bore of the coupling is $5\frac{1}{2}$ in.

396.—A leather-faced cone clutch, similar to that shown in Fig. 218 of the Text, has a large diameter of $15\frac{1}{4}$ in., a face of $3\frac{1}{8}$ in., and a cone-face angle of 10 deg. The compression spring consists of 6.5 turns of $\frac{1}{4}$- by $\frac{9}{32}$-in. steel wire, the outer diameter of the coils being $2\frac{5}{16}$ in. The free length of the spring is $4\frac{7}{16}$ in., and when in place in the clutch, its length is $2\frac{15}{16}$ in. Assuming the motor runs at 1,200 r.p.m. and that the coefficient of friction is 0.2, determine the following: (a) The horsepower that may be transmitted. (b) The normal pressure per square inch of cone surface. (c) The magnitude of the design constants K and K_1.

397.—The motor of a light motor car is equipped with a leather-faced cone clutch having a large diameter of 10 in., a face of $1\frac{3}{4}$ in., and a cone-face angle of 12.5 deg. Assuming the normal pressure per square inch of cone surface as 13 lb., and that the coefficient of friction is 0.20, determine the following: (a) The horsepower that may be transmitted at 1,500 r.p.m. (b) The size of wire, the number of coils, the outside diameter and free length of the spring, assuming that due to the construction used, the outside diameter of the spring cannot exceed $3\frac{3}{4}$ in. and the inside diameter cannot be less than $2\frac{7}{8}$ in.; furthermore, the length of the spring when the clutch is engaged is limited to $2\frac{1}{2}$ in.

398.—A 3½- by 5-in. six-cylinder motor has a maximum rating of 47.7 hp. at 2,000 r.p.m. The horsepower and revolutions per minute corresponding to the maximum torque are 37 and 1,250 respectively. This motor is to be equipped with a leather-faced cone clutch having a large diameter of 13¾ in., a face of 2½ in., and a cone-face angle of 12.5 deg.; determine the following: (a) The spring pressure that is necessary to engage the clutch, assuming the coefficient of friction is 0.2. (b) The normal pressure per square inch of cone surface. (c) The magnitude of the design constants K and K_1.

399.—A 4¼- by 5¼-in. four-cylinder motor has a maximum rating of 35.7 hp. at 1,520 r.p.m. The horsepower and revolutions per minute corresponding to the maximum torque are 28.8 and 960 respectively. This motor is to be equipped with a leather-faced cone clutch having a large diameter of 14⅞ in., a face of 2½ in., and a cone-face angle of 12.5 deg. Determine the following: (a) The spring pressure that is necessary to engage the clutch, assuming the coefficient of friction is 0.2. (b) The normal pressure per square inch of cone surface. (c) The magnitude of the design constants K and K_1.

400.—A 5- by 6-in. four-cylinder motor has a maximum rating of 53.0 hp. at 1,500 r.p.m. The horsepower and revolutions per minute corresponding to the maximum torque are 20.6 and 400 respectively. The motor is equipped with an asbestos-fabric-faced cone clutch having a large diameter of 14.91 in., a face of 2.5 in. and a cone-face angle of 11 deg. Determine the following, having given the pressure exerted by the spring upon the cones as 275 lb.: (a) The magnitude of the design constants K and K_1. (b) The normal pressure per square inch of cone surface. (c) The magnitude of the coefficient of friction.

401.—In a 4¾- by 5½-in. four-cylinder motor, the horsepower and revolutions per minute corresponding to the maximum torque are 65 and 1,300 respectively. The motor is equipped with a cone clutch, both elements of which are made of cast iron. The small diameter of the cone is 14⅜ in., its face is 2.6 in. and the cone-face angle is 10 deg. Having given the pressure exerted by the spring upon the cones as 500 lb., determine the following: (a) The magnitude of the design constants K and K_1. (b) The normal pressure per square inch of cone surface. (c) The magnitude of the coefficient of friction.

COUPLINGS AND CLUTCHES

402.—A cone clutch, having a tarred-fiber-faced cone in contact with a steel-casting shell, transmits 50 hp. at 800 r.p.m. The small and large diameters of the cone are 8 and 10.5 in. respectively, and the face is 5.25 in. Determine the following: (a) The spring pressure that is necessary to engage the clutch, assuming the coefficient of friction is 0.15. (b) The normal pressure per square inch of cone surface. (c) The magnitude of the design constants K and K_1.

403.—A $3\frac{3}{4}$- by 5-in. six-cylinder motor has a maximum rating of 56 hp. at 1,700 r.p.m. The horsepower and revolutions per minute corresponding to the maximum torque are 38.1 and 1,000 respectively. The motor is equipped with a leather-faced cone clutch having a large diameter of 15 in., a face of $2\frac{5}{8}$ in. and a cone-face angle of 12.5 deg. Determine the following, having given the spring pressure upon the cones as 362 lb. (a) The normal pressure per square inch of cone surface. (b) The magnitude of the design constants K and K_1. (c) The magnitude of the coefficient of friction.

404.—A $4\frac{1}{4}$- by $5\frac{1}{4}$-in. six-cylinder motor has a maximum rating of 53.0 hp. at 2,000 r.p.m. The horsepower and revolutions per minute corresponding to the maximum torque are 39.7 and 1,000 respectively. This motor is to be equipped with a leather-faced cone clutch having a large diameter of $14\frac{7}{8}$ in., a face of $2\frac{1}{2}$ in., and a cone-face angle of 12.5 deg. Determine the following: (a) The spring pressure that is necessary to engage the clutch, assuming the coefficient of friction is 0.2. (b) The normal pressure per square inch of cone surface. (c) The magnitude of the design constants K and K_1.

405.—In a double-cone clutch hoisting drum, similar to the one shown in Fig. 223 of the Text, the tangential load upon the 8-in. drum is 1,000 lb. The mean diameter of the double cones is 14 in., the angle 2α is 34 deg. 40 min., and the working face of the wood blocks is $2\frac{3}{16}$ in. long. The engaging screw h has three threads per inch, has a mean diameter of 1.08 in., and is operated by a 12-in. lever. The thrust collar e has a mean diameter of $3\frac{3}{32}$ in. The pressure due to the spring l is 425 lb., and the mean diameter of the spring cage m is $2\frac{7}{8}$ in. Assuming that the coefficient of friction for the wood facing of the clutch is 0.3, that for the screw as 0.06, and that for the thrust collar and the spring cage as 0.1, determine the following: (a) The force required on the operating lever in order to raise the load on the drum. (b) The horsepower necessary to drive the drum so as to hoist the load at 100 ft. per minute assuming the efficiency of the hoist as 85 per cent. (c) The size of Ewart detachable chain required, assuming that the cones are bolted onto a chain sprocket approximately $19\frac{1}{2}$ in. in diameter, in place of a gear as shown in Fig. 223.

406.—A disk clutch, similar to the one shown in Fig. 230 of the Text, is capable of transmitting 4 hp. at 100 r.p.m. The driving disk, faced with hard maple blocks, is 10 in. in diameter, has a face of 2 in. and is fastened to the pulley by four $\frac{1}{2}$- by $1\frac{1}{2}$-in. cap screws, equally spaced on a $11\frac{1}{8}$-in. circle. Determine the following: (a) The magnitude of the design constants K_2 and K_3. (b) The normal pressure per square inch of disk surface, assuming the coefficient of friction is 0.3. (c) The shearing stress in each of the cap screws used for fastening the disk to the pulley.

407.—A plate clutch, the design of which is somewhat similar to that shown in Fig. 230 of the Text, is capable of transmitting 138 hp. at 100 r.p.m. The driving disk, faced with heavy friction paper and maple plug inserts, is 48 in. in diameter and $17\!/_{64}$ in. thick, has a $4\frac{1}{2}$-in. face and is fastened to a cast-iron hub by means of eighteen $\frac{3}{4}$- by $2\frac{1}{4}$-in. cap screws equally spaced on a $12\frac{1}{2}$-in. circle. Determine the following: (a) The magnitude of the design constants K_2 and K_3. (b) The normal pressure per square inch of disk surface, assuming the coefficient of friction is 0.3. (c) The shearing and bearing stresses coming upon each cap screw used for fastening the disk to the cast-iron hub.

408.—The statement of this problem is identical with that of Prob. 407, with the exception that the clutch transmits 62 hp. and that the driving disk is 36 in. in diameter and $13\!/_{64}$ in. thick, has a $3\frac{5}{8}$-in. face and is fastened to a cast-iron hub by means of fourteen $\frac{3}{4}$- by $1\frac{1}{2}$-in. cap screws equally spaced on a $9\frac{3}{4}$-in. circle.

409.—A hydraulic disk clutch of the Metten type has the driving head faced with Thermoid disks of 3-in. face and 37-in. outside diameter. The steel-casting driving head is fastened to the steel frame by twenty-three $\frac{7}{8}$-in. bolts located on a $38\frac{1}{2}$-in. bolt circle. The $\frac{1}{4}$-in. steel driven disk is fastened to the flange on the shaft by eight $1\frac{1}{8}$-in. fitted bolts located on an $8\frac{3}{4}$-in. bolt circle.

COUPLINGS AND CLUTCHES

The clutch is capable of transmitting 1,070 hp. at 350 r.p.m. Assuming the unbalanced area subjected to a working oil pressure of 65 lb. per square inch as equivalent to the area of a 32½-in. circle, determine the following: (a) The apparent coefficient of friction at the surface in contact. (b) The shearing and bearing stresses in the bolts used for fastening the driven disk. (c) The tension in the bolts used for fastening the driving head to the steel frame.

410.—A slip coupling similar to that shown in Fig. 233 of the Text has a 3¾-in. bore and is capable of transmitting 25 hp. at 100 r.p.m. Assuming that each of the springs is compressed ⅜ in., determine the following: (a) The unit pressure at the surfaces in contact and the probable coefficient of friction at these surfaces. (b) The tensile and shearing stresses in the coupling bolts.

411.—The statement of this problem is identical with that of Prob. 410, with the exception that the bore is 3¼ in. and that 8 hp. are transmitted.

412.—The statement of this problem is identical with that of Prob. 410, with the exception that the bore is 4¼ in. and that 40 hp. are transmitted.

413.—The statement of this problem is identical with that of Prob. 410, with the exception that the bore is 6 in., the horsepower transmitted is 100 and the spring compression is ⅝ in.

414.—The statement of this problem is identical with that of Prob. 410, with the exception that the bore is 4⅝ in. and that 50 hp. are transmitted.

415.—A 3¾- by 5¼-in. six-cylinder motor has a maximum rating of 57.7 hp. at 2,000 r.p.m. The horsepower and revolutions per minute corresponding to the maximum torque are 41 and 1,050 respectively. This motor is equipped with a multiple-disk clutch having asbestos-fabric-faced disks whose large and small diameters are 8½ in. and 6¼ in. respectively. Determine the spring pressure that is necessary to engage the clutch, assuming five driving and five driven disks are used, and that the coefficient of friction is 0.22.

416.—A 4⅛- by 5¼-in. six-cylinder motor has a maximum rating of 64.5 hp. at 1,800 r.p.m. The horsepower and revolutions per minute corresponding to the maximum torque are 25 and 500 respectively. This motor is equipped with a multiple-disk clutch having asbestos-fabric-faced disks whose large and small diameters are 8½ in. and 6¼ in. respectively. The spring pressure required to apply the clutch is 300 lb. Assuming that the coefficient of friction is 0.24, determine the number of driving disks, and the magnitude of the design constants K_2 and K_3.

417.—A 6¼- by 7-in. four-cylinder motor has a maximum rating of 70 hp. at 850 r.p.m. The horsepower and revolutions per minute corresponding to the maximum torque are 60 and 650 respectively. The motor is equipped with a multiple-disk clutch having 14 soft steel and 14 cast-brass disks, whose large and small diameters are 11⅝ in. and 9 in. respectively. In this clutch the pressure of the spring is multiplied by a system of toggle levers having a ratio of 4 to 1. The spring consists of seven coils of 7/16-in. steel wire, the outer diameter of the coils being 3⅞ in. The free length of the spring is 5⅜ in. Assuming the coefficient of friction is 0.05, determine the following: (a) The spring pressure required to engage the clutch. (b) The amount the spring will have to be compressed to give the necessary pressure. (c) The magnitude of the design constants K_2 and K_3.

418.—A disk clutch, similar to the one shown in Fig. 234 of the Text, is capable of transmitting 7.5 hp. at 100 r.p.m. The driving disks are 9⅛ in. in diameter and have a face of 2 5/16 in. Determine the following: (a) The magnitude of the design constants K_2 and K_3. (b) The normal pressure per square inch of disk surface, assuming the coefficient of friction as 0.08.

419.—The statement of this problem is identical with that of Prob. 418, with the exception that the clutch transmits 20 hp. and that the driving disks are 13¼ in. in diameter and have a 3 5/16-in. face.

420.—A disk clutch, similar to that shown in Fig. 235 of the Text, is capable of transmitting 10 hp. at 100 r.p.m. The driving disks are 10 in. in diameter and have a 1.5-in. face. Determine the following: (a) The magnitude of the design constants K_2 and K_3. (b) The normal pressure per square inch of disk surface, assuming the coefficient of friction as 0.3.

421.—The statement of this problem is identical with that of Prob. 420, with the exception that the clutch transmits 25 hp. and that three disks 15¾ in. in diameter of 2-in. face are used.

COUPLINGS AND CLUTCHES

422.—The large diameter and face of the disks of the clutch shown in Fig. 236 of the Text are 10 in. and 1 in. respectively. The compression spring contains 9.5 coils of ⅜-in. steel wire, the outer diameter of the coils being 3⅛ in. The free length of the spring is 7¼ in. and when in place with the clutch engaged, the length is 5⅛ in. Determine the following, assuming the motor runs at 1,200 r.p.m. and that the coefficient of friction is 0.13: (a) The horsepower that the clutch will transmit. (b) The normal pressure per square inch of disk surface and the magnitude of the design constants K_2 and K_3.

423.—The transmission on a motor truck is equipped with a multiple-disk clutch similar in design to that shown in Fig. 237 of the Text. Determine the horsepower transmitted by the clutch and the magnitude of the design constants K_2 and K_3, having given the following data: (a) The revolutions per minute of the motor are 1,050. (b) The outer and inner diameter of the five asbestos-fabric-faced driving disks are 8⁷⁄₁₆ in. and 6¼ in. respectively. (c) The coefficient of friction is 0.16. (d) The large clutch spring consists of 5.25 coils of ⁵⁄₁₆-in. steel wire, the outer diameter of the coils being 4⅛ in. The free length of this spring is 5 in. and when in place with the clutch engaged, the length is 1⅞ in. (e) The small spring is made up of 4.5 coils of ⁵⁄₁₆-in. steel wire, the outside diameter of the coils being 3⁵⁄₁₆ in. The free length of this spring is 3⅛ in., and when in place with the clutch engaged, the length is 2¼ in.

424.—A motor, delivering 100 hp. at 1,000 r.p.m., is equipped with a Hele-Shaw clutch containing 33 disks having a mean diameter of 11 in. Determine the spring pressure required to engage the clutch, assuming the coefficient of friction as 0.08 and that the groove angle is 35 deg. Also determine the unit pressure upon the surfaces in contact, assuming that 860 sq. in. of groove surface are in actual contact.

425.—The statement of this problem is identical with that of Prob. 424, with the exception that the clutch transmits 80 hp. and that twenty-seven 11-in. disks, having a contact area of 700 sq. in., are used.

426.—The statement of this problem is identical with that of Prob. 424, with the exception that the clutch transmits 50 hp. and that twenty-nine 8½-in. disks, having a contact area of 560 sq. in., are used.

427.—The statement of this problem is identical with that of Prob. 424, with the exception that the clutch transmits 30 hp. and that twenty-nine 6½-in. disks, having a contact area of 430 sq. in., are used.

428.—A Hele-Shaw clutch containing 25 disks having a mean diameter of 16 in. is used on a light locomotive, the motor of which runs at 750 r.p.m. The compression spring consists of 7¾ coils of ½-in. steel wire, the outer diameter of the coils being 6 in. The free length of the spring is 8 in. and when in place with the clutch engaged, the length is 5 in. Assuming that 90 per cent. of the spring force is actually used in forcing the plates together, determine the following: (a) The total pressure produced by the spring. (b) The horsepower that may be transmitted, assuming the coefficient of friction is 0.08 and the groove angle is 35 deg.

429.—A single band clutch similar to the one shown in Fig. 258 of the Text, is used on a hoisting engine transmitting 600 hp. at 60 r.p.m. The diameter of the clutch ring is 80 in. and the total angle of contact of the basswood blocks is 291.5 deg. Determine the following: (a) The foot-pounds of energy transmitted per minute per square inch of actual contact, having given the face of the blocks as 9 in. (b) The average intensity of the normal pressure per square inch of block, assuming the coefficient of friction as 0.3. (c) The maximum and minimum tensions in the 9- by ⅝-in. steel band to which the blocks are fastened. (d) The stress in the band, assuming the cross-section of the band is weakened by two ⅝-in. rivets. (e) The shearing stress and the bearing pressure on the 2½- by 1¾-in. trunnions of the adjusting block to which the band is anchored. (f) The compressive stress in the 2½-in. adjusting screw, assuming that the latter has three square threads per inch, and that the screw makes an angle of 78 deg. 40 min. with the vertical center line shown in Fig. 258.

430.—For the Moore and White combined conical-disk clutch shown in Fig. 244 of the Text, derive an expression for the moment M that may be transmitted, assuming D denotes the mean diameter of the disks; P, the total axial force produced by the toggle mechanism; S, the total force exerted by the springs; 2α, the angle of the groove in the ring e; μ, the coefficient of friction for all friction surfaces.

SECTION XIII

BRAKES

431.—In Fig. 42 is shown a double-block brake used on the driving shaft of a traveling crane girder. The brake sheave makes 120 r.p.m. and the coefficient of friction may be assumed as 0.33. Determine the following: (a) The number of foot-

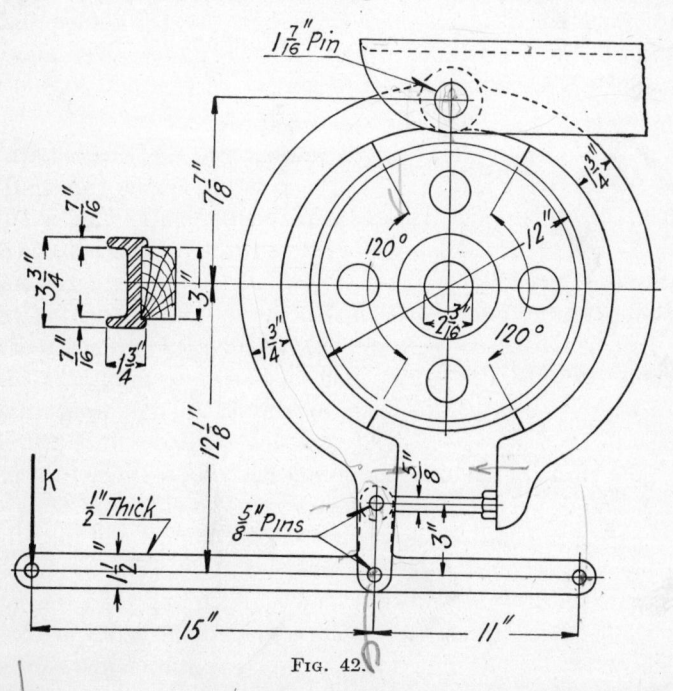

Fig. 42.

pounds of energy absorbed per square inch of actual block surface in contact with the sheave, assuming the force K is 50 lb. (b) The pressure coming upon each block in pounds per square inch of projected area. (c) The stress produced in the eye-bolt.

432.—(a) Calculate the horsepower absorbed by the brake shown in Fig. 265 of the Text, assuming the following data: $a = 12$ in.; $c = 9\frac{1}{2}$ in.; $d = 3$ in.; $e = f = 7\frac{1}{2}$ in.; $g = 9\frac{1}{2}$ in.;

the brake sheave is 10 in. in diameter and runs at 300 r.p.m.; the force $K = 35$ lb.; the angle $2\theta = 90$ deg.; the coefficient of friction is 0.35. (b) Determine the number of foot-pounds of energy absorbed per square inch of actual block surface, if the face of the blocks is 2 in.

433.—For the double-block brake shown in Fig. 43 determine the following, having given that the force K, due to the dead weight, has a magnitude of 35 lb., that the coefficient of friction is 0.35, and that the brake pulley runs at 400 r.p.m.: (a) The

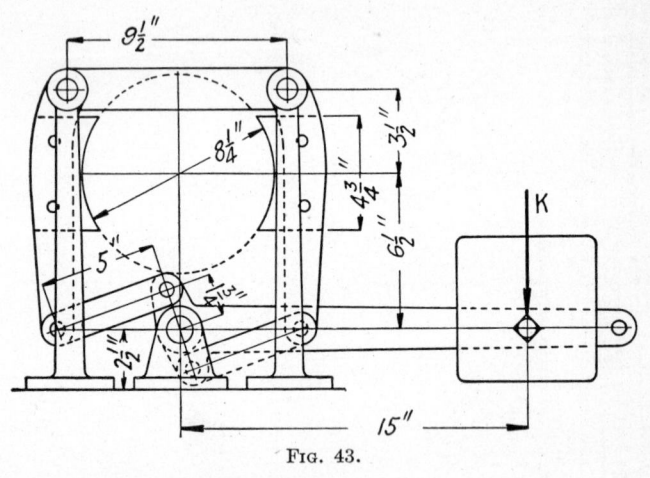

Fig. 43.

horsepower that the brake is capable of absorbing. (b) The foot-pounds of energy absorbed per square inch of actual contact surface, assuming the face of the blocks is 2 in.

434.—The following data applies to the post brake shown in Fig. 266 of the Text: The magnitude of the force K is 3,300 lb., the revolutions per minute of the brake sheave is 50 and its diameter is 13 ft., and the coefficient of friction is 0.35. Assuming the rotation of the sheave as clockwise, determine by means of graphics, the tangential resistance exerted upon the brake sheave by each block, and calculate the foot-pounds of energy absorbed per square inch of actual block contact, assuming the face of the blocks is 8 in.

435.—For a simple band brake, similar to the one shown in Fig. 268 of the Text, determine the magnitude of the force K required to hold the load on the drum, having given the following data. $a = 66$ in.; $b = 6$ in.; the angle of contact between the brake band and the sheave is 260 deg.; the coefficient of friction is 0.25; the diameter of the brake sheave is 32 in.; the diameter of the hoisting drum to which the brake sheave is attached is 20 in.; the tangential load on the drum is 2,100 lb. (*b*) If the brake band is $\frac{3}{16}$ in. thick determine its width assuming the permissible stress as 8,000 lb. per square inch.

436.—In a band brake, similar to the one shown in Fig. 268 of the Text, the angle of contact θ is 250 deg.; the diameter of the

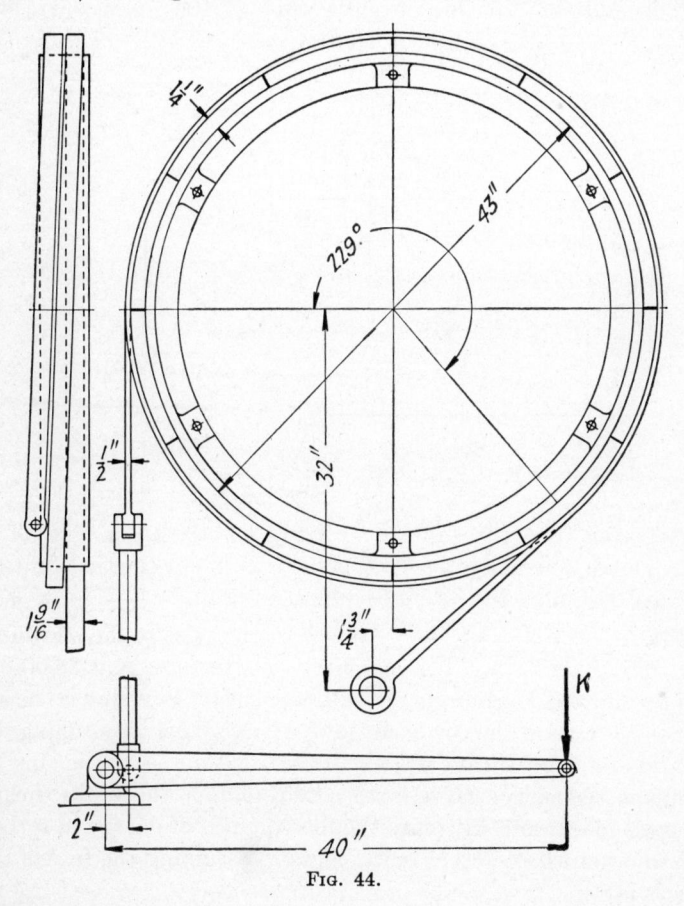

Fig. 44.

brake sheave is $11\frac{1}{2}$ in.; the dimensions *a* and *b* are $16\frac{1}{2}$ in. and $2\frac{1}{8}$ in. respectively; the width and thickness of the brake band are 2 in. and $\frac{3}{16}$ in. respectively. Assuming the coefficient of friction is 0.18, calculate the magnitude of the force *K* and the twisting moment on the brake sheave for both directions of rotation, so that the maximum stress in the band shall not exceed 8,000 lb. per square inch.

437.—For the simple band brake shown in Fig. 269 of the Text, determine the tangential force that the brake is capable of exerting on the brake sheave, also the stress in the band, having given the following data: (*a*) The diameter d of the brake sheave is $27\frac{1}{2}$ in. (*b*) The magnitude of the force K due to the dead weight is 95 lb. (*c*) The total angle of contact, between the brake band and the sheave, is 618 deg. (*d*) The coefficient of friction is 0.25. (*e*) The dimensions a, b, and c are 24 in., $3\frac{1}{2}$ in. and 21 in. respectively. (*f*) The brake band is 1 in. wide and $\frac{1}{2}$ in. thick, and the screws used for fastening the blocks to the band are $\frac{5}{16}$ in. in diameter.

438.—Having given the tangential force on the sheave of the band brake shown in Fig. 44 as 3,600 lb., determine the following: (*a*) The force K required at the end of the operating lever in order to prevent the load from running down, assuming counter-clockwise rotation of the brake sheave and that the coefficient of friction is 0.20. (*b*) The stress in the brake band assuming $\frac{5}{16}$-in. screws are used for fastening the wood blocks to the band.

439.—A band brake similar to the one shown in Fig. 270 of the Text is located on the armature shaft of a direct-connected electric drum elevator. Determine the twisting moment that the brake is capable of resisting, having given the following data: $a = 12$ in.; $b = 1\frac{1}{2}$ in.; the angle of contact is 270 deg.; the coefficient of friction is 0.30; the magnitude of the force K is 50 lb.; the diameter of the brake sheave is 12 in.

440.—A hoisting engine of 1,000 hp. is equipped with a crank disk band brake similar to the one shown in Fig. 270 of the Text. Determine the magnitude of the force K required to stop the engine, having given the following data: $a = 12$ in.; $b = 6$ in.; the angle of contact is 300 deg.; the coefficient of friction is 0.35; the engine runs at 50 r.p.m. and the diameter of the crank disk is 84 in. (*b*) Determine the thickness of the brake band if the width is 6 in. and the permissible stress is 10,000 lb. per square inch.

441.—The shaft of a band brake, similar to the one shown in Fig. 269 of the Text, is geared to the main hoisting motor of an 80-ton traveling crane. The gear ratio between the motor and the brake shaft is 5 to 1, and the motor is capable of delivering 50 hp. at 380 r.p.m. (a) Calculate the magnitude of the force K required to apply the brake having given the following data: $a = 24$ in.; $b = 3\frac{1}{2}$ in.; $d = 27\frac{1}{2}$ in.; the total angle of contact between the band and the brake sheave is 618 deg.; the coefficient of friction is 0.25 and the rotation of the sheave is clockwise. (b) Determine the stress in the 1- by $\frac{1}{2}$-in. brake band assuming $\frac{5}{16}$-in. screws are used for fastening the wood blocks to the band. (c) Using the stress found in (b), determine the size of the adjusting screw at the end of the band.

442.—For the differential band brake shown in Fig. 271 of the Text, we have given the following data: $a = 12$ in.; $b = 2$ in.; $c = 5$ in.; $d = 28$ in.; the angle of contact = 298 deg.; the size of the band is $3\frac{1}{8}$ in. by $\frac{3}{16}$ in. Determine the magnitude of the force K and the twisting moment on the brake shaft so that the band shall not be subjected to a stress exceeding 8,000 lb. per square inch, assuming the coefficient of friction is 0.2.

443.—A shaft, transmitting 15 hp. at 500 r.p.m., is equipped with a cone brake which is applied by means of a spring and released by a solenoid. Determine the axial force required to apply the brake and the units normal pressure, having given the following data: (a) The large diameter of the cone is 12 in. and its face is $1\frac{3}{4}$ in. (b) The coefficient of friction is 0.35. (c) The angle $\alpha = 12$ deg.

444.—A shaft, transmitting 24 hp. at 200 r.p.m., is equipped with a disk brake similar to that shown in Fig. 273 of the Text. Determine the force required on a 15-in. handwheel in order to apply the brake, having given the following data: (a) The mean diameter of the four steel and five fiber disks is 10 in. (b) The screw has six threads per inch and a mean diameter of $1\frac{3}{4}$ in. (c) The coefficient of friction for the disks is 0.18 and for the screw 0.10. (d) The mean diameter of the thrust bearing between d and g is 3 in., and the coefficient of friction for this bearing is 0.12. (e) Assume the moment of friction, due to the journal and pivot friction on the pinion, as equivalent to 5 per cent. of the total moment transmitted by the pinion.

445.—A shaft transmitting 18 hp. at 180 r.p.m. is equipped with a disk brake similar to the one shown in Fig. 273 of the Text. Having given the following data, determine the number of steel and fiber disks to be used, in order that a force of 30 lb. applied on the 15-in. handwheel is capable of setting the brake. (*a*) The mean diameter of the screw is 1½ in. and its pitch is ⅛ in. (*b*) The coefficient of friction for the disks is 0.20 and for the screw is 0.10. (*c*) The mean diameter of the disks is 10 in. and that of the thrust bearing between *d* and *g* is 2¾ in. (*d*) The coefficient of friction for this thrust bearing is 0.12. (*e*) Assume the moment of friction due to the journal and pivot friction on the pinion as equivalent to 6 per cent. of the total moment transmitted by the pinion.

446.—For the load brake shown in Fig. 274 (*a*) of the Text, derive an expression for D, the mean diameter of the friction disks that will make the hoist self-locking, also an expression for $(P)R$, the moment required to lower the load, having given the following notation: W denotes the tangential load on the worm wheel; R, the radius of the hand sheave; d, the mean diameter of the worm; α, the angle of the mean helix of the worm; φ', the apparent angle of friction for the worm; μ, the coefficient of friction for the discs.

447.—For the Niles brake shown in Fig. 275 of the Text, derive expressions for the following, using as far as possible the notation given in Art. 334. (*a*) Axial thrust on the helical clutch jaws during the hoisting period. (*b*) The condition for self-locking for hoisting. (*c*) The maximum and minimum axial thrust on the helical jaws during the lowering period. (*d*) The condition for self-locking for lowering. (*e*) The moment required to release the brake.

448.—For the Pawlings and Harnischfeger brake shown in Fig. 276 of the Text, derive expressions for the following, using as far as possible the notation given in Art. 334. (*a*) The axial thrust on the screw during the hoisting period. (*b*) The condition for self-locking for hoisting. (*c*) The maximum and minimum axial thrust on the screw during the lowering period. (*d*) The condition for self-locking for lowering. (*e*) The moment required to release the brake.

449.—For the Case brake shown in Fig. 277 of the Text, derive expressions for the following, using as far as possible the notation given in Art. 334. (*a*) The axial thrust on the screw during the hoisting period. (*b*) The condition for self-locking for hoisting. (*c*) The maximum and minimum axial thrust on the screw during the lowering period. (*d*) The condition for self-locking for lowering. (*e*) The moment required to release the brake.

450 to 455.—In Fig. 45 is shown the general arrangement of the hoisting equipment used on the trolley of an electric traveling crane, equipped with a mechanical load brake. In Table 16 are given the leading dimensions of one size of the several load brakes shown in Figs. 275, 276, 277 and 278 of the Text respectively. The data given in the last column apply to a brake, which is practically the same as that shown in Fig. 276, with the exception

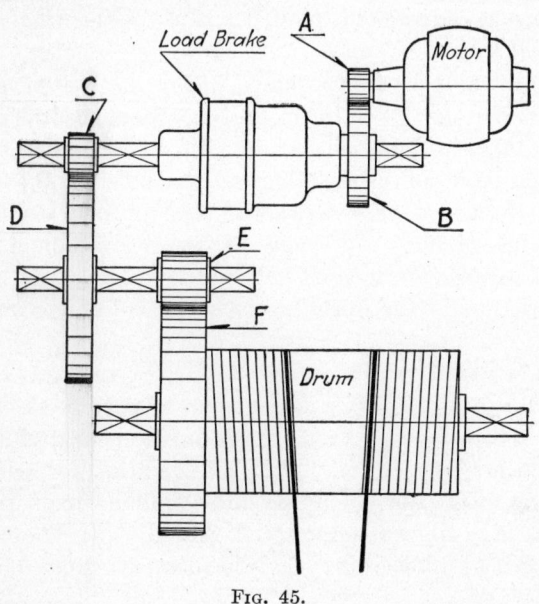

FIG. 45.

that wood-block facing is used for the friction disks in place of fiber. In analyzing these load brakes use the following general data: (1) The acceleration of the rope, running on or off the drum, is 2 feet per second per second. (2) The angle of friction for the helical surfaces is equivalent to 5 deg. (3) The efficiency of each pair of gears including the bearings is 92 per cent. (4) The efficiency of the drum including the bearings is 90 per cent.

Using the data, given in Table 16, pertaining to the particular load brake assigned for analysis, determine the following: (a) The efficiency of the pulley arrangement between the drum and the hook for both raising and lowering of the load. (b) The combined efficiency of the mechanism between the brake and the hook. (c) The axial thrust on the helical surfaces while hoisting the load; also while lowering the load. (d) The condition for self-locking for both hoisting and lowering of the load. (*e*) The moment required to release the brake. (*f*) The axial thrust per square inch of projected area of the disks. (*g*) The axial thrust per square inch of projected area of the helical surfaces. (*h*) The foot-pounds of energy absorbed per minute per square inch of disk surfaces in contact. (*i*) The apparent torsional stress in the brake shaft. (*j*) The actual horsepower required for hoisting the rated load.

TABLE 16

		Problem number				
		450	**451**	**452**	**453**	**454**
Capacity of crane, tons		10	10	10	10	10
Motor	Horsepower	25	18	25	18	20
	Revolutions per minute	590	460	575	520	700
Diameter of drum, inches		17	14.75	16.25	18	15
Number and size of ropes supporting the load		6–9/16	4–5/8	4–5/8	4–3/4	4–5/8
Number of sheaves on hook block		3	2	2	2	2
Friction disks	Outer diameter, inches	13	11	13 15/16	10 1/2	10 11/16
	Inner diameter, inches	7 1/8	3 1/4	8	6 1/4	4 9/16
Helical surfaces	Outer diameter, inches	5 1/4	2 5/8	3 5/8	5	3 1/8
	Inner diameter, inches	2 7/8	2 1/8	2 7/8	3	2 3/8
Lead of mean helix, inches		1 5/8	1 5/8	3	4	1 3/4
Diameter of the brake shaft, inches		2 7/8	2 1/8	2 7/8	2 7/8	2 3/8
Coefficient of disk friction		0.1	0.25	0.1	0.1	0.3
Number of teeth and diametral pitch	Gear *A*	14–3	16–4	14–4	15–3.5	13–4
	Gear *B*	58–3	58–4	50–4	64–3.5	62–4
	Gear *C*	......	14–3	12–3	17–3	16–3
	Gear *D*	......	58–3	42–3	78–3	58–3
	Gear *E*	13–2.5	12–2	15–2	17–2.5	12–2
	Gear *F*	95–2.5	42–2	57–2	72–2.5	42–2

SECTION XIV

SHAFTING AND BEARINGS

455.—On a 10-ton traveling crane, the 18-in. hoisting drum is similar in design to that shown in Fig. 284 of the Text. Determine the fiber stress in the $2\frac{3}{4}$-in. shaft, which in this case is cast into the drum and has a running fit in the bearings A and B which are 9 in. long. The following data applies to this drum: $b = 6\frac{1}{2}$ in.; $c = 34\frac{1}{4}$ in.; $e = 8$ in.; $f = 7\frac{1}{16}$ in.; $g = 36$ in.; $L = 72$ in.; $t = 8$ in.; each rope load W is 5,150 lb.; the tangential force on the 30-in. gear acts vertically upwards and has a magnitude of 6,880 lb.; the weight of the drum is 930 lb.; the weight of the gear is 425 lb.; the weight of the shaft is 125 lb. Determine the unit bearing pressures at A and B, assuming the diameter of the shaft in the bearings is $2\frac{1}{2}$ in.

456.—On a 40-ton traveling crane, the 24-in. hoisting drum is similar in design to that shown in Fig. 284 of the Text. Determine the fiber stress in the $3\frac{3}{4}$-in. shaft, which in this case is cast into the drum and has a running fit in the bearings A and B which are $10\frac{1}{2}$ in. long. The following data applies to this drum: $b = 6$ in.; $c = 31\frac{9}{16}$ in.; $e = f = 9\frac{1}{8}$ in.; $g = 36\frac{1}{16}$ in.; $L = 72\frac{1}{8}$ in.; $t = 10\frac{1}{8}$ in.; each rope load W is 14,000 lb.; the tangential force on the 36-in. gear acts vertically upwards and has a magnitude of 20,200 lb.; the weight of the drum is 2,250 lb.; the weight of the gear is 830 lb.; the weight of the shaft is 260 lb. Determine the unit bearing pressures at A and B assuming the diameter of the shaft in the bearings is $3\frac{1}{2}$ in.

457.—On a 60-ton traveling crane, the 30-in. hoisting drum is similar in design to that shown in Fig. 284 of the Text. Determine the fiber stress in the $4\frac{1}{4}$-in. shaft, which in this case is cast into the drum and has a running fit in the bearings A and B which are $12\frac{1}{2}$ in. long. The following data applies to this drum: $b = 10$ in.; $c = 37\frac{5}{8}$ in.; $e = f = 12\frac{1}{4}$ in.; $g = 42\frac{5}{8}$ in.; $L = 85\frac{1}{4}$ in.; $t = 12\frac{1}{4}$ in.; each rope load W is 16,000 lb.; the tangential force on the 48-in. gear acts vertically upwards and has a magnitude of 20,000 lb.; the weight of the drum is 2,500 lb.; the weight of the gear is 1,650 lb.; the weight of the

94 PROBLEMS IN MACHINE DESIGN

shaft is 350 lb. Determine the unit bearing pressures at A and B assuming the diameter of the shaft in the bearings is 4 in.

458 to 462.—In Fig. 46(a) is shown one end of a standard electric railway car-axle and Table 17 contains general dimensions pertaining to four sizes of axles as well as the capacities in pounds

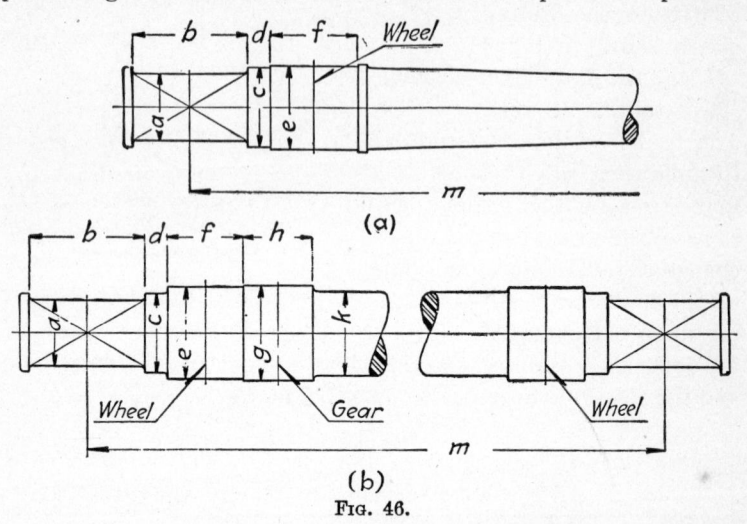

FIG. 46.

per axle for which they were designed. Using the data, given in Table 17, relating to the particular axle to be analyzed, determine the following: (a) The maximum fiber stress produced in the sections where there is a change in the diameter. (b) The maximum bearing pressure coming upon each journal. (c) The horsepower lost in friction at the journals, assuming the coefficient of journal friction is 0.05, the speed of the car 15 miles per hour and the diameter of the wheels 33 in.

TABLE 17

Problem number	Capacity, pounds	Dimensions, inches						
		a	b	c	d	e	f	m
458	15,000	$3\frac{3}{4}$	7	$4\frac{3}{4}$	$2\frac{1}{2}$	$5\frac{1}{8}$	$7\frac{11}{16}$	75
459	22,000	$4\frac{1}{4}$	8	$5\frac{1}{4}$	2	$5\frac{3}{4}$	$7\frac{11}{16}$	75
460	31,000	5	9	$6\frac{1}{8}$	2	$6\frac{1}{2}$	$7\frac{11}{16}$	76
461	38,000	$5\frac{1}{2}$	10	$6\frac{5}{8}$	2	7	$7\frac{11}{16}$	77

SHAFTING AND BEARINGS

462 to 466.—A standard electric railway car motor-axle is shown in Fig. 46(b), and in Table 18 are given the general dimensions of four sizes in addition to the capacity in pounds per axle for which they were designed. The location of the motor pinion M relative to the driving gear G is clearly shown in Fig. 47.

Using the data, given in Table 18, pertaining to the particular axle to be analyzed, determine the following: (a) The maximum fiber stress in the various sections of the axle where there is a change in diameter. (b) The maximum bearing pressure coming upon each journal. (c) The horsepower lost in friction at the journals, assuming the coefficient of journal friction is 0.05 and the speed of the car as 15 miles per hour.

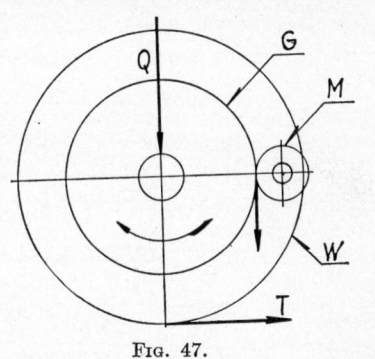

FIG. 47.

TABLE 18

		Problem number			
		462	463	464	465
Capacity per axle, pounds			15,000	22,000	31,000	38,000
Tractive effort on wheel, pounds			2,900	4,200	5,700	9,600
Diameter of wheel, inches			33	33	36	36
Number of teeth and pitch, gear			67–3	73–3	59–2.5	64–2.5
Dimensions, inches	a	3¾	4 ¼	5	5 ½
	b	7	8	9	10
	c	4¾	5 ¼	6 ⅛	6 ⅝
	d	2½	2	2	2
	e	5 7/16	5 15/16	6 15/16	7 15/16
	f	7½	7 ½	6 ½	6 ½
	g	5½	6	7	8
	h	6⅛	6 ⅛	6 ⅛	6 ⅛
	k	4½	5 ½	6 ½	7
	m	75	75	76	77

0.2% Carbon

466.—A mild carbon-steel shaft, transmitting 15 hp. at 210 r.p.m., is supported on two bearings 27 in. apart and has keyed to it two gears. The pinion, having 18 teeth of 3 diametral pitch, is located 5 in. to the right of the right-hand bearing and delivers the power horizontally to the right. The gear, having 80 teeth of 4 diametral pitch, is located 6 in. to the right of the left-hand bearing and receives the power in a horizontal direction above the shaft. Calculate the diameter of the shaft, assuming a working stress equal to 30 per cent. of the stress at the elastic limit.

467.—A mild carbon-steel shaft, transmitting 15 hp. at 210 r.p.m., is supported on two bearings 27 in. apart and has keyed to it two gears. The pinion, having 18 teeth of 3 diametral pitch, is located 5 in. to the left of the right-hand bearing and delivers the power horizontally to the right. The gear, having 80 teeth of 4 diametral pitch, is located 6 in. to the right of the left-hand bearing and receives the power in a vertical direction from below. Calculate the diameter of the shaft, assuming a working stress equivalent to 35 per cent. of the stress at the elastic limit.

468.—A nickel-steel shaft, transmitting 30 hp. at 275 r.p.m., is supported on two bearings 25 in. apart and has keyed to it two gears. The pinion, having 18 teeth of 3 diametral pitch, is located 6 in. to the right of the right-hand bearing and delivers the power vertically downwards. The gear, having 63 teeth of $3\frac{1}{2}$ diametral pitch, is located 6 in. to the left of the left-hand bearing and receives the power in a horizontal direction below the shaft. Calculate the diameter of the shaft, assuming a working stress equal to 35 per cent. of the stress at the elastic limit.

469.—The statement of this problem is identical with that of Prob. 468, with the exception that the pinion delivers the power horizontally to the right.

470.—A mild carbon-steel shaft, transmitting 20 hp. at 210 r.p.m., is supported on two bearings 30 in. apart and has keyed to it two gears. The pinion, having 18 teeth of 3 diametral pitch, is located 6 in. to the right of the right-hand bearing and delivers the power horizontally to the right. The gear, having 80 teeth of 4 diametral pitch, is located 6 in. to the right of the left-hand bearing and receives the power in a horizontal direction above the shaft. Calculate the diameter of the shaft, assuming a working stress equal to 35 per cent. of the stress at the elastic limit.

471.—The statement of this problem is identical with that of Prob. 470, with the exception that the pinion is located to the left of the right-hand bearing.

472.—A nickel-steel shaft, transmitting 25 hp. at 275 r.p.m., is supported on two bearings 21 in. apart and has keyed to it two gears. The pinion, having 18 teeth of 3 diametral pitch, is located 5 in. to the right of the right-hand bearing and delivers the power vertically downwards. The gear, having 63 teeth of $3\frac{1}{2}$ diametral pitch, is located 6 in. to the left of the left-hand bearing and receives the power in a horizontal direction below the shaft. Calculate the diameter of the shaft, assuming a working stress equal to 35 per cent. of the stress at the elastic limit.

473.—A nickel-steel shaft, transmitting 25 hp. at 275 r.p.m., is supported on two bearings 21 in. apart and has keyed to it two gears. The pinion, having 18 teeth of 3 diametral pitch, is located 5 in. to the left of the right-hand bearing and delivers the power vertically downwards. The gear, having 63 teeth of $3\frac{1}{2}$ diametral pitch, is located 6 in. to the right of the left-hand bearing and receives the power in a horizontal direction below the shaft. Calculate the diameter of the shaft, assuming a working stress equal to 35 per cent. of the stress at the elastic limit.

474.—A mild carbon-steel shaft, transmitting 30 hp. at 270 r.p.m., is supported on two bearings 25 in. apart and has keyed to it a gear C and two pinions D and E. The gear C, receiving power vertically from above, has 54 teeth of 3 diametral pitch and is located $5\frac{1}{2}$ in. to the left of the left-hand bearing. The pinion D, delivering 50 per cent. of the total power horizontally to the left, has 20 teeth of 4 diametral pitch and is located 5 in. to the left of the right-hand bearing. The pinion E, delivering the remainder of the power horizontally to the left, has 20 teeth of 4 diametral pitch and is located 5 in. to the right of the right-hand bearing. Calculate the diameter of the shaft, assuming a working stress equal to 27 per cent. of the stress at the elastic limit.

475.—The statement of this problem is identical with that of Prob. 474, with the exception that the gear C is located to the right of the left-hand bearing.

476.—A nickel-steel shaft, transmitting 40 hp. at 240 r.p.m., is supported on two bearings 12 in. apart and has keyed to it a gear C and two pinions D and E. The gear C, receiving power vertically from below, has 80 teeth of 4 diametral pitch and is located midway between the bearings. The pinion D, delivering 50 per cent. of the total power vertically upwards, has 24 teeth of 3 diametral pitch and is located 6 in. to the left of the left-hand bearing. The pinion E, delivering the remainder of the power vertically upwards, has 24 teeth of 3 diametral pitch and is located 6 in. to the right of the right-hand bearing. Calculate the diameter of the shaft, assuming a working stress equal to 40 per cent. of the stress at the elastic limit.

477.—The statement of this problem is identical with that of Prob. 476, with the exception that the gear C receives power in a horizontal direction.

478.—A mild carbon-steel shaft, transmitting 40 hp. at 270 r.p.m., is supported on two bearings 27 in. apart and has keyed to it a gear C and two pinions D and E. The gear C, receiving power vertically from above, has 60 teeth of 3 diametral pitch and is located 6 in. to the left of the left-hand bearing. The pinion D, delivering 50 per cent. of the total power horizontally to the left, has 21 teeth of $3\frac{1}{2}$ diametral pitch and is located $5\frac{1}{2}$ in. to the left of the right-hand bearing. The pinion E, delivering the remainder of the power horizontally to the left, has 21 teeth of $3\frac{1}{2}$ diametral pitch and is located $5\frac{1}{2}$ in. to the right of the right-hand bearing. Calculate the diameter of the shaft, assuming a working stress equal to 33 per cent. of the stress at the elastic limit.

479.—The statement of this problem is identical with that of Prob. 478, with the exception that the gear C is located to the right of the left-hand bearing and that it receives power horizontally from the right.

480.—A nickel-steel shaft, transmitting 30 hp. at 210 r.p.m., is supported on two bearings 12 in. apart, and has keyed to it a gear C and two pinions D and E. The gear C, receiving power vertically from below, has 80 teeth of 4 diametral pitch and is located midway between the bearings. The pinion D, delivering 50 per cent. of the total power vertically upwards has 24 teeth of 3 diametral pitch and is located 6 in. to the left of the left-hand bearing. The pinion E, delivering the remainder of the power vertically upwards, has 24 teeth of 3 diametral pitch and is located 6 in. to the right of the right-hand bearing. Calculate the diameter of the shaft, assuming a working stress equal to 40 per cent. of the stress at the elastic limit.

481.—The statement of this problem is identical with that of Prob. 480, with the exception that the gear C receives power vertically from above.

482.—A mild carbon-steel shaft, transmitting 20 hp. at 250 r.p.m., is supported on two bearings 16 in. apart and has keyed to it two gears. The spur pinion, having 24 teeth of 3 diametral pitch, is located $5\frac{1}{2}$ in. to the left of the left-hand bearing and delivers power horizontally to the left. The bevel gear, having 42 teeth of $3\frac{1}{2}$ diametral pitch is located 7 in. to the left of the right-hand bearing and receives power in a vertical direction from below. The thrust upon the shaft, due to the bevel gear, is towards the left. Calculate the diameter of the shaft, assuming a working stress equal to 33 per cent. of the stress at the elastic limit, and that the face of the bevel gear is $2\frac{1}{2}$ in.

483.—A mild carbon-steel shaft, transmitting 15 hp. at 225 r.p.m., is supported on two bearings 24 in. apart and has keyed to it two gears. The spur pinion, having 21 teeth of $3\frac{1}{2}$ diametral pitch, is located 6 in. to the right of the left-hand bearing and delivers the power vertically downwards. The bevel gear, having 48 teeth of 4 diametral pitch is located 7 in. to the left of the right-hand bearing and receives the power in a horizontal direction above the shaft. The thrust upon the shaft, due to the bevel gear, is towards the left. Calculate the diameter of the shaft assuming a working stress equal to 33 per cent. of the stress at the elastic limit, and that the face of the bevel gear is $2\frac{3}{8}$ in.

484.—A mild carbon-steel shaft, transmitting 25 hp. at 300 r.p.m., is supported on two bearings 20 in. apart and has keyed to it two gears. The spur pinion, having 21 teeth of 3 diametral pitch, is located 6 in. to the right of the left-hand bearing and delivers power horizontally to the right. The bevel gear, having 49 teeth of $3\frac{1}{2}$ diametral pitch is located $6\frac{1}{2}$ in. to the left of the right-hand bearing and receives the power in a horizontal direction below the shaft. The thrust upon the shaft, due to the bevel gear, is towards the left. Calculate the diameter of the shaft, assuming a working stress equal to 35 per cent. of the stress at the elastic limit, and that the face of the bevel gear is 2¾ in.

485.—A hollow steel shaft transmits 8,000 hp. at 600 r.p.m. Having given the length of shaft as 25 ft. and its outside and inside diameters as 10 in. and 5 in. respectively, and that the modulus of elasticity for torsion is 10,000,000, determine the working stress in the shaft and the angular deflection in degrees.

486.—A hollow steel shaft transmits 10,000 hp. at 500 r.p.m. Having given the length of the shaft as 30 ft. and its outside and inside diameters as 11 in. and 5½ in. respectively, determine the working stress in the shaft and the angular deflection in degrees, assuming the modulus of elasticity for torsion is 10,000,000.

487.—A hollow nickel-steel shaft, whose outside diameter is twice the inside diameter, transmits 2,000 hp. at 220 r.p.m. Assuming that the bending moment coming upon the shaft is 1.5 times the torsional moment transmitted, determine the following: (a) The size of the shaft, assuming a working stress equal to 40 per cent. of the stress at the elastic limit. (b) The size of a solid shaft for the same conditions. (c) The per cent. saved in weight by the use of the hollow shaft.

488.—A hollow nickel-steel shaft, whose outside diameter is twice the inside diameter, transmits 3,600 hp. at 210 r.p.m. Having given the bending moment coming upon the shaft as equivalent to 1.6 times the torsional moment, determine the following: (a) The size of the shaft, assuming 12,000 lb. per square inch as the permissible stress. (b) The size of a solid shaft for the same condition. (c) The per cent saved in weight by the use of the hollow shaft.

489.—A flywheel, weighing 2,450 lb. and having a radius of gyration of 30 in., is running at 240 r.p.m. Upon shutting down of the power which was used for driving the wheel, it was observed that 645 revolutions were made before the flywheel came to a stop. Having given the bore as 6 in., determine the coefficient of friction assuming the following conditions: (a) Uniformly distributed pressure. (b) Normal wear proportional to the work of friction.

490.—(a) For the conical journal, shown in Fig. 48, determine the expression for the magnitude of the thrust Q produced upon the adjustable collar by the load P, assuming the normal wear is proportional to the work of friction. (b) Having given the following data: $P = 7,000$ lb.; $a = 7$ in.; $b = 6$ in.; $c = 5\frac{1}{2}$ in.; $d = 8$ in.; $l = 8\frac{1}{2}$ in.; calculate the magnitude of the end thrust Q and the total horsepower absorbed by friction in the journal

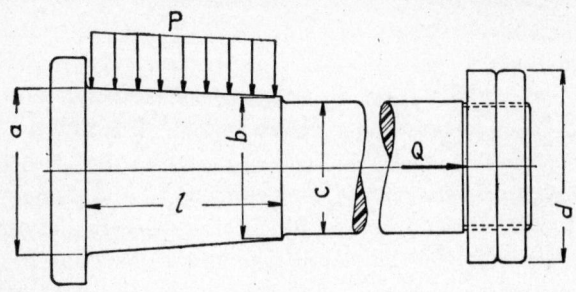

Fig. 48.

and at the collar, assuming the coefficient of friction is 0.06 and the revolutions per minute are 40.

491.—For the spherical pivot, shown in Fig. 49, derive an expression for the moment of friction assuming the following condi-

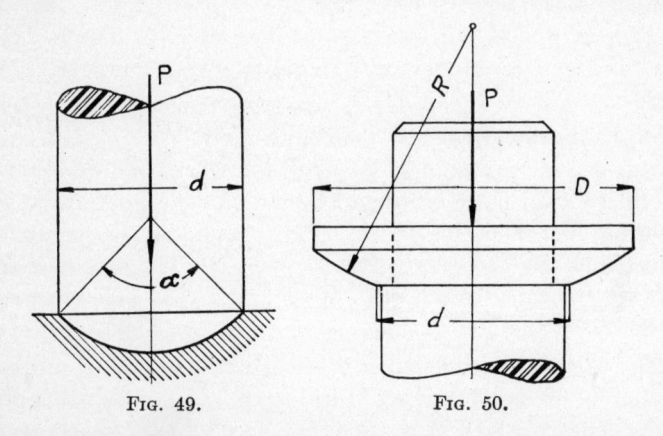

Fig. 49.   Fig. 50.

tions: (a) Uniformly distributed pressure. (b) Normal wear proportional to the work of friction. NOTE.—For both conditions assume $\alpha = 90$ deg.

492.—For a spherical pivot, similar to the one shown in Fig. 49, and having a subtended angle α equal to 180 deg., derive an expression for the moment of friction for each of the following conditions: (a) Uniformly distributed pressure. (b) Normal wear proportional to the work of friction.

493.—For the spherical pivot, shown in Fig. 50, derive an expression for the moment of friction for each of the following conditions. (a) Uniformly distributed pressure. (b) Normal wear proportional to the work of friction.

494.—The bevel gear and pinion, on the rear axle of a motor car are arranged as shown in Fig. 51. The gear has 53 teeth of 5 pitch, and the pinion has 13 teeth. The face of both gears is $1\frac{5}{16}$ in. and the dimensions a and b indicated in Fig. 51 are $3\frac{1}{4}$ in. and $5\frac{1}{2}$ in. respectively. Assuming the teeth to be of the standard 20 deg. involute type and that 35 hp. is transmitted at 1,500 r.p.m. of the pinion, determine the following: (a) The resultant tooth pressure and the magnitude of the thrusts along

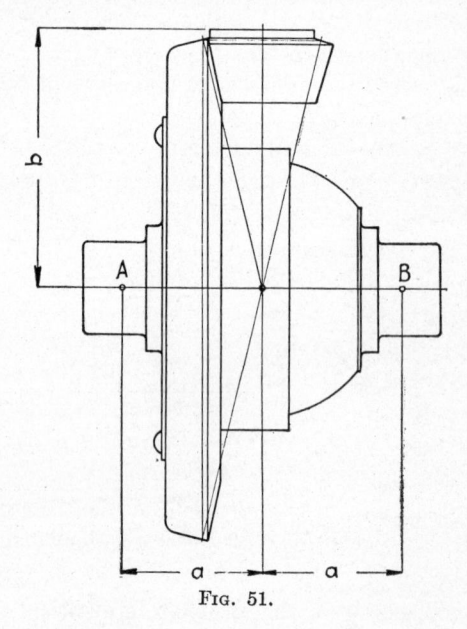

Fig. 51.

the shafts. (b) The resultant pressures coming upon the bearings A and B. (c) The type and size of Gurney ball bearing that should be used at A and B.

495.—The bevel gear and pinion, on the rear axle of a motor car, are arranged as shown in Fig. 51. The gear has 52 teeth of 5 pitch, and the pinion has 13 teeth. The face of both gears is $1\frac{1}{4}$ in. and the dimensions a and b are $2\frac{7}{8}$ in. and $5\frac{1}{4}$ in. respectively. Assuming the teeth to be of the standard 20 deg. involute type and that 30 hp. is transmitted at 1,500 r.p.m. of the pinion, determine the following: (a) The resultant tooth pressure and the magnitude of the thrusts along the shafts. (b) The resultant pressures coming upon the bearings A and B. (c) The type and size of Gurney ball bearing that should be used at A and B.

496.—The motor of a truck is capable of developing 24 hp. at 1,100 r.p.m. but only 90 per cent. of this power is available at the worm shaft of the worm-gear drive on the rear axle. The speed reduction in the transmission is 3.06 to 1. The worm has a pitch diameter of $2\frac{1}{2}$ in., a divided pitch of $1\frac{3}{16}$ in., and a lead of $5\frac{11}{16}$ in. The pitch diameter of the worm wheel is 7.77 in. Having given the pressure angle of the worm thread as 25 deg., and the coefficient of friction for the worm and gear as 0.02, determine the following: (a) The loads coming upon the worm shaft bearings, having given the distance between these bearings as $6\frac{1}{8}$ in. (b) The type and size of Gurney ball bearings that must be used on the worm shaft. (c) The loads coming upon the worm-gear bearings, having given the distance between these bearings as $4\frac{3}{4}$ in. (d) The type and size of Gurney ball bearings that must be used on the worm gear.

497.—For the worm-gear drive described in Prob. 377 determine the following: (a) The loads coming upon the worm-shaft bearings, having given the distance between these bearings as 12.93 in. (b) The type and size of Gurney ball bearings that must be used on the worm shaft. (c) The loads coming upon the worm-gear bearings having given the distance between these bearings as 9.758 in. (d) The type and size of Gurney ball bearings that are required on the worm gear.

498.—The statement of this problem is identical with that of Prob. 497, with the exception that the worm-gear drive described in Prob. 378 be used.

499.—The statement of this problem is identical with that of Prob. 497, with the exception that the worm-gear drive described in Prob. 379 be used.

500.—In the worm-gear speed-reducer described in Prob. 380 the plain bearings are to be replaced by ball bearings, determine the following: (a) The loads coming upon the worm-shaft bearings and the type and size of Gurney ball bearings that should be used. (b) The loads coming upon the worm-gear bearings and the type and size of Gurney ball bearings that should be used. (c) By means of a neatly executed sketch, giving important dimensions, show how the bearings selected are installed in the speed-reducer.

501.—The statement of this problem is identical with that of Prob. 500, with the exception that the speed-reducer described in Prob. 381 be used.

502.—The statement of this problem is identical with that of Prob. 500, with the exception that the speed-reducer described in Prob. 382 be used.

503.—The statement of this problem is identical with that of Prob. 500, with the exception that the speed-reducer described in Prob. 383 be used.

504.—The statement of this problem is identical with that of Prob. 500, with the exception that the speed-reducer described in Prob. 384 be used.

SECTION XV

GENERAL PROBLEMS

505.—For the hook and yoke, shown in Fig. 52, determine the following, having given the capacity of the hook as 10 tons: (*a*) The stresses in the pin. (*b*) The stresses in the yoke. (*c*) The stresses in the threaded shank of the hook, as well as

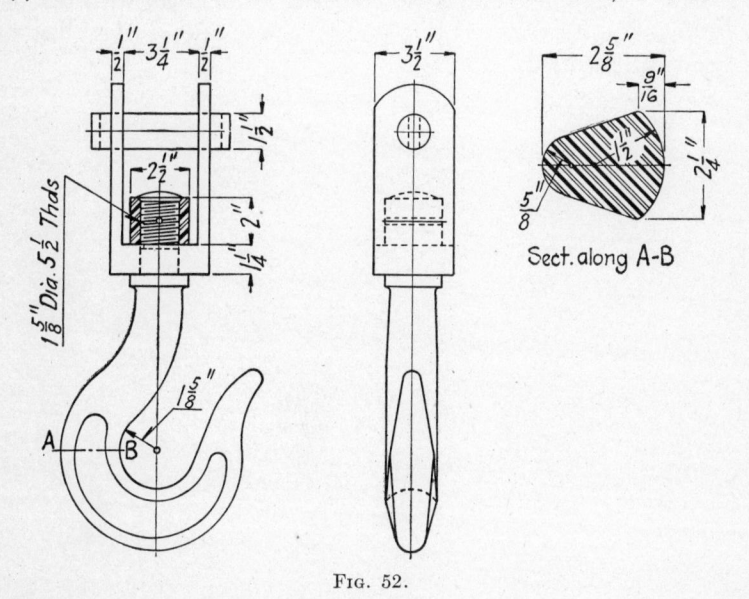

Fig. 52.

those on the nut. (*d*) The stresses in the body of the hook along the section AB.

506.—(*a*) Determine the capacity of the hook and block, shown in Fig. 53, having given the following data: The permissible stresses in tension, shearing and compression for the steel used in the construction of the block are 12,000, 9,000 and 18,000 lb. per square inch respectively. (*b*) What size of 6 by 19 plow-steel wire rope must be used for the capacity determined in (*a*), assuming a factor of safety of five and further that the block shown is used on a derrick, the boom of which contains two head sheaves of the same size as that used on the hook block?

507.—In a hand-operated crane, having a capacity of 20 tons, the hook block is arranged as shown in Fig. 54. Having given the size of the coil chain for reefing the block as 1 in., the coefficient of chain and journal friction as 0.2 and 0.08 respectively,

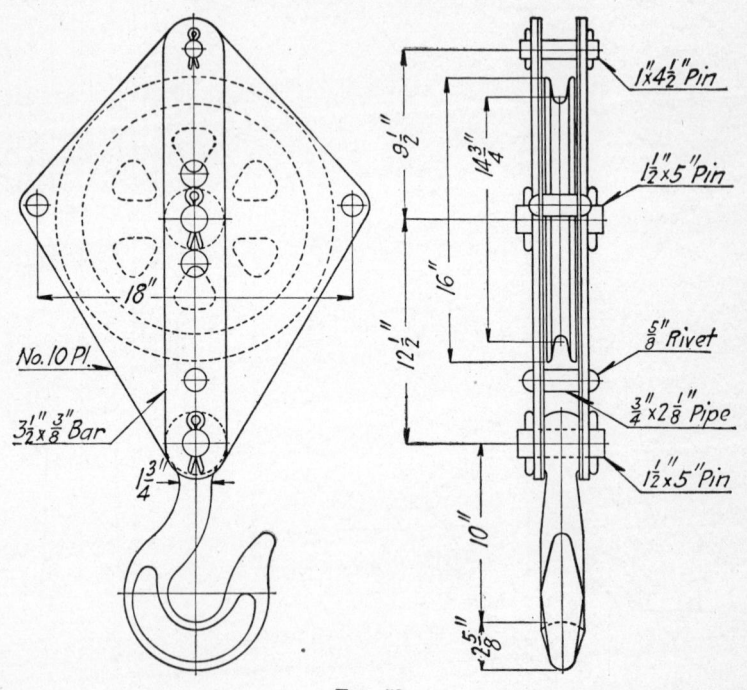

Fig. 53.

determine the following, assuming the full load is suspended from the hook: (a) The load coming upon each of the sheave pins, also the tensile, shearing and bearing stresses coming upon these pins. (b) The tensile, shearing and bearing stresses produced in the trunnions supporting the hook. (c) The tensile stress in the shank of the hook, assuming six threads per inch are used. (d) The tensile and compressive stresses produced in the principal section of the hook.

508.—In the motor-driven car puller, shown in Fig. 55, determine the following, assuming the motor is operated at its rated capacity: (a) The stresses in the teeth of the motor pinion and gear, assuming 14.5-deg. involute cut teeth are used. (*b*) The stresses in the teeth of the various gears used in the planetary gear train assuming cast teeth. (*c*) The loads coming upon the pins supporting the intermediate gears, also the magnitude of

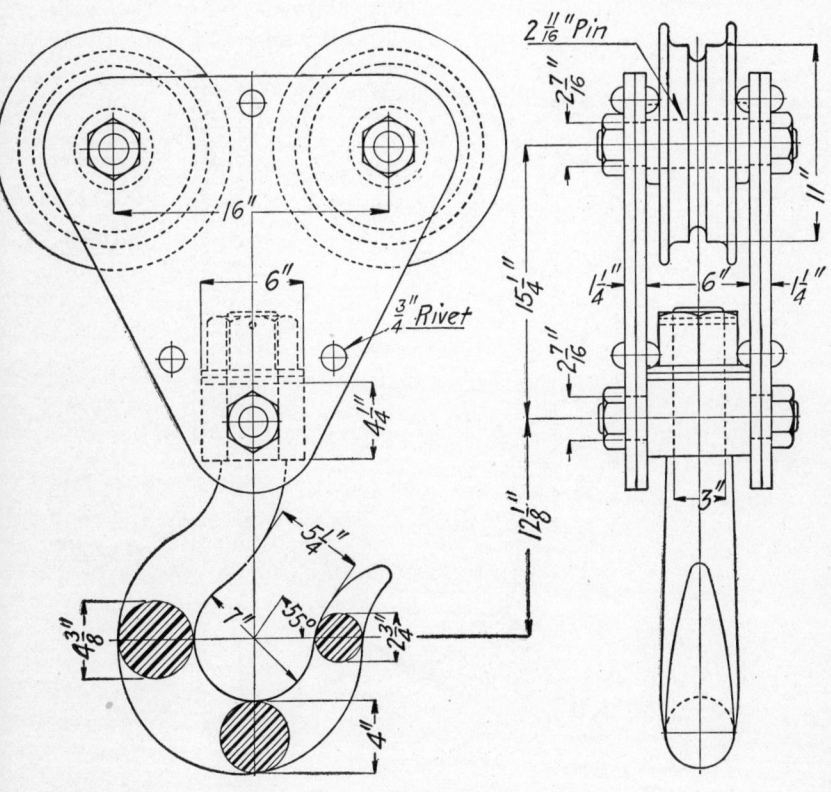

FIG. 54.

the bearing and shearing stresses produced in these pins, assuming the diameter of the threaded portion is 1½ in. (*d*) The tangential force that can be produced on the capstan, also the velocity of this force in feet per minute. (*e*) The maximum stress produced in the main shaft of the machine and the magnitude of the bearing pressures coming upon this shaft.

509.—The power-driven car puller, shown in Fig. 56, has a maximum capacity for pulling 12 loaded cars. Assuming the force Q, required to pull the 12 cars, has a magnitude of 6,000 lb. and that the manila rope used is given three full turns around the

Fig. 55.

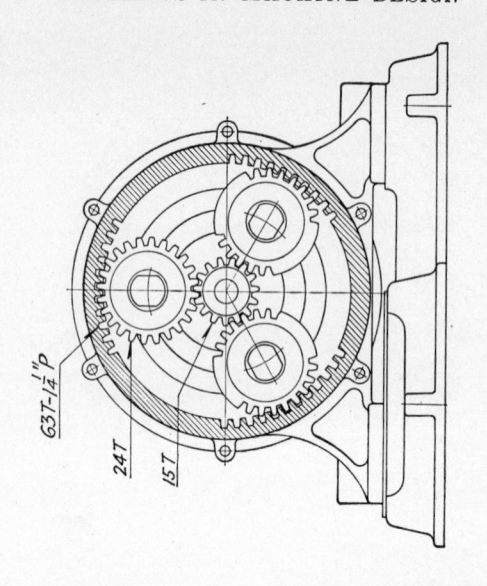

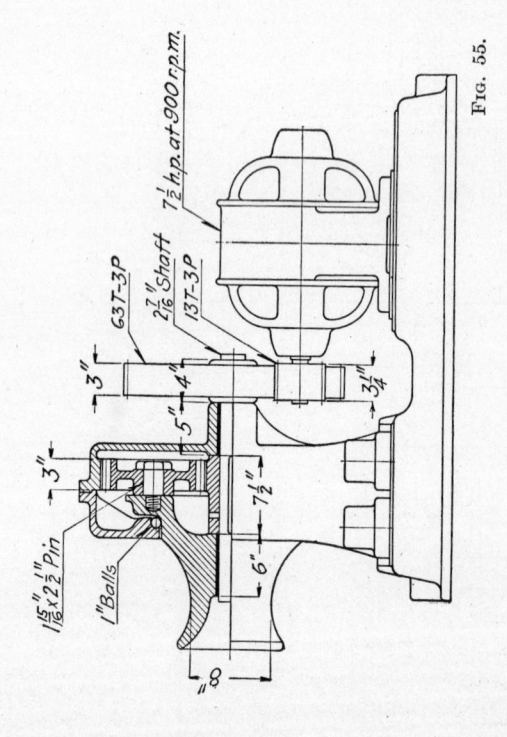

Fig. 56.

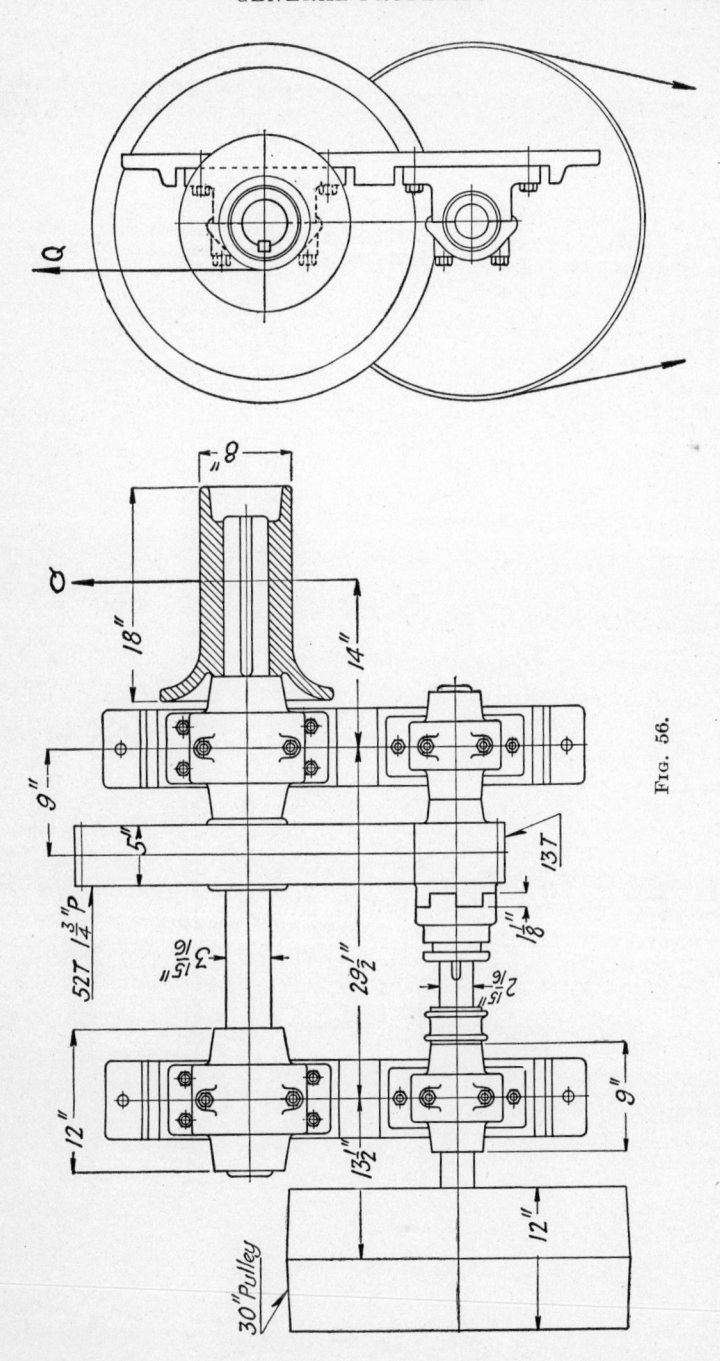

capstan, determine the following: (a) The size of manila rope required, using a factor of safety of three. (b) The pull required on the free end of the rope, assuming the coefficient of friction between the rope and capstan as 0.25. (c) The maximum stress produced in the capstan shaft and the unit pressures coming upon the various bearings supporting this shaft. (d) The size of belt required to drive the machine, assuming the motor has a 6 in. pulley and is located 10 ft. from the center of the driving shaft of the car puller. (e) The size and speed of the motor required to operate the car puller. (f) The maximum stress produced in the driving shaft, also the unit pressures coming upon the various bearings supporting this shaft. (g) The stresses in the gear teeth and the horsepower lost due to tooth friction, assuming the gears have cast teeth of the 15-deg. involute type and that the coefficient of friction for the teeth is 0.16. (h) The total horsepower lost in the machine due to friction in the bearings and gears, assuming the coefficient of journal friction as 0.08. (i) The probable efficiency of the car puller.

510.—The shaft-straightening press, shown in Fig. 57, has a capacity for bending or straightening $3\frac{1}{2}$-in. shafts. The steel operating screw is 2 in. in diameter and has four square threads per inch. The nut for the screw is made of cast iron and is $5\frac{1}{4}$ in. long. The maximum distance between the sliding supports A and B, used for supporting the shaft, is $31\frac{1}{2}$ in. Determine the following: (a) The force required on the screw in order to straighten $3\frac{1}{2}$-in. shafting, assuming the elastic limit of the material is 48,000 lb. per square inch. (b) The compressive and bearing stresses coming upon the operating screw. (c) The tensile and shearing stresses in the cast-iron nut. (d) The force required at the end of a 36-in. lever in order to turn the screw, assuming the coefficient of friction for the thread is 0.12. (e) The tensile and compressive stresses in the frame along the section CD.

511.—In the mandrel press, shown in Fig. 58, the pinion, meshing with the rack cut directly on the operating plunger, is 1 in. in diameter and has 12 cut teeth of the 14.5-deg. involute type. Assuming the load P applied on the operating lever is 160 lb., determine the following: (a) The magnitude of the various stresses produced in the sections along AB and CD. (b) The stresses produced in the teeth of the pinion and the rack, having given the face of the latter as $1\frac{11}{16}$ in. (c) The bending stress

GENERAL PROBLEMS 111

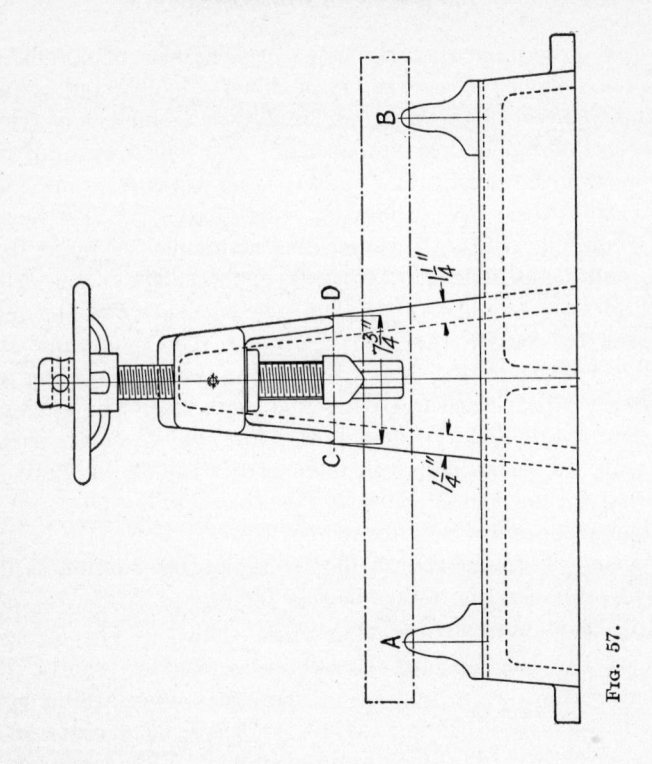

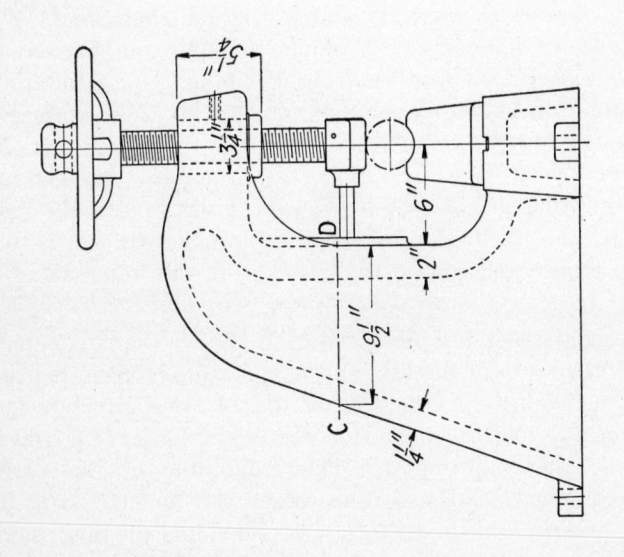

Fig. 57.

112   PROBLEMS IN MACHINE DESIGN

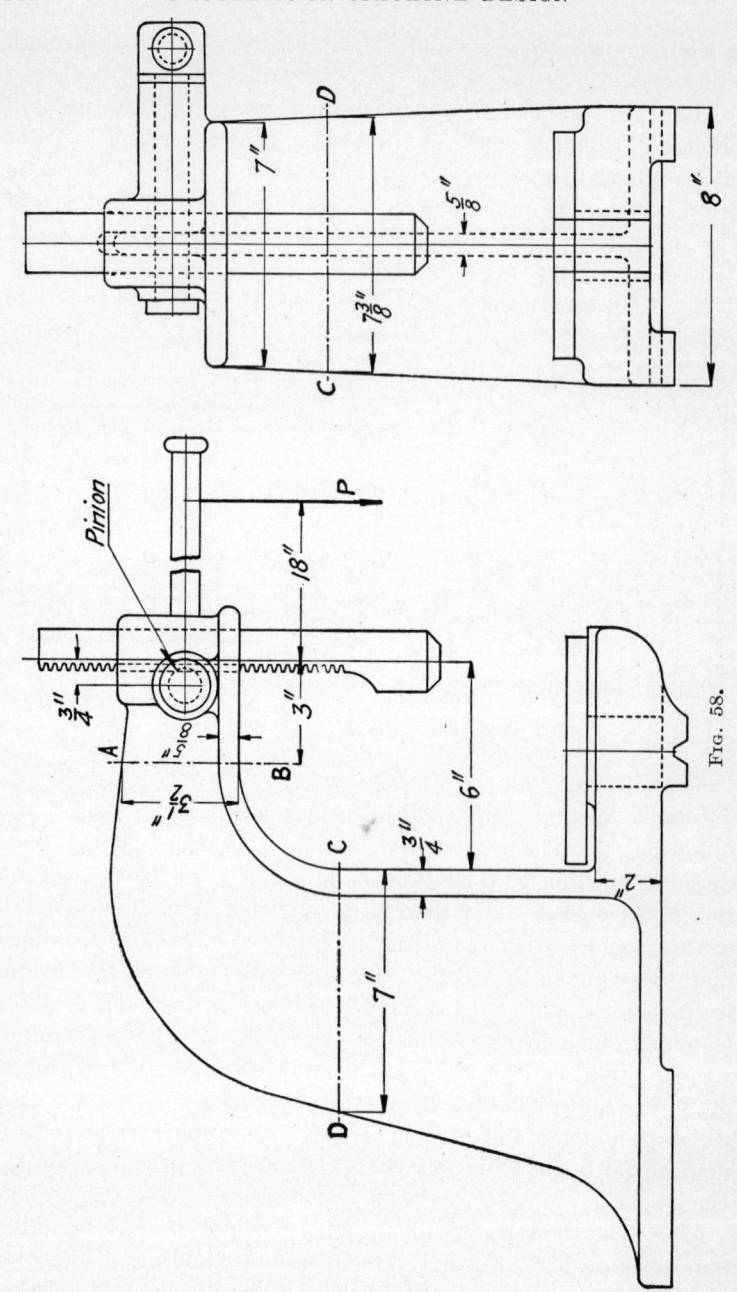

Fig. 58.

in the operating lever, assuming the diameter of the boss, through which the lever passes, is 2 in.

512.—In Fig. 59 are shown the contructive details used in bracing the bulged plate of the header that is located in front of the steam drum of a certain water-tube boiler. The steam drum has an outside diameter of 35⅛ in. and a shell thickness of 7/16 in. The longitudinal joint of the drum is of the triple-riveted butt-joint type, having ⅜-in. strap plates and ⅞-in. rivets. The long pitch used in this joint is 7¾ in. and the inner and outer back-pitches are 2 in. and 2¾ in. respectively. Assum-

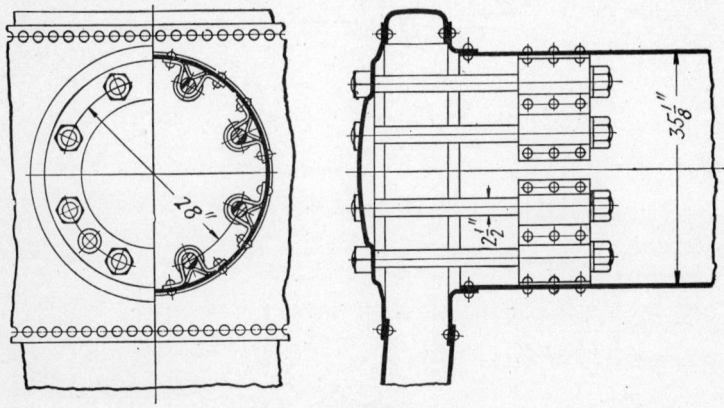

Fig. 59.

ing the steam pressure is 250 lb. per square inch, determine the following: (a) The tensile, shearing and bearing stresses produced in the longitudinal joint of the drum. (b) The maximum tensile stress produced in the 2½-in. stay-rods, assuming the pitch of the threads as ¼ in. and that the unbraced area of the bulged plate is equivalent to the cross-sectional area of the drum. (c) The maximum stresses produced in the ⅞-in. rivets used for fastening the U-plate anchors to the shell. (d) The maximum stresses produced in the U-plate anchors, assuming they are made of ½-in. material. (e) Determine the factor of safety with which this boiler is operating, basing it upon the stresses recommended for boiler design by the American Society of Mechanical Engineers.

513.—The hoisting cylinder, of the compressed-air-operated bracket crane shown in Fig. 60, has an inner and outer diameter of 6 3/16 in. and 6⅝ in. respectively. The air pressure carried

114   PROBLEMS IN MACHINE DESIGN

in the cylinder is 100 lb. per square inch and the maximum radius of the hook is 11 ft. 5 in. It is required to investigate the stresses and pressures produced in the various parts of the

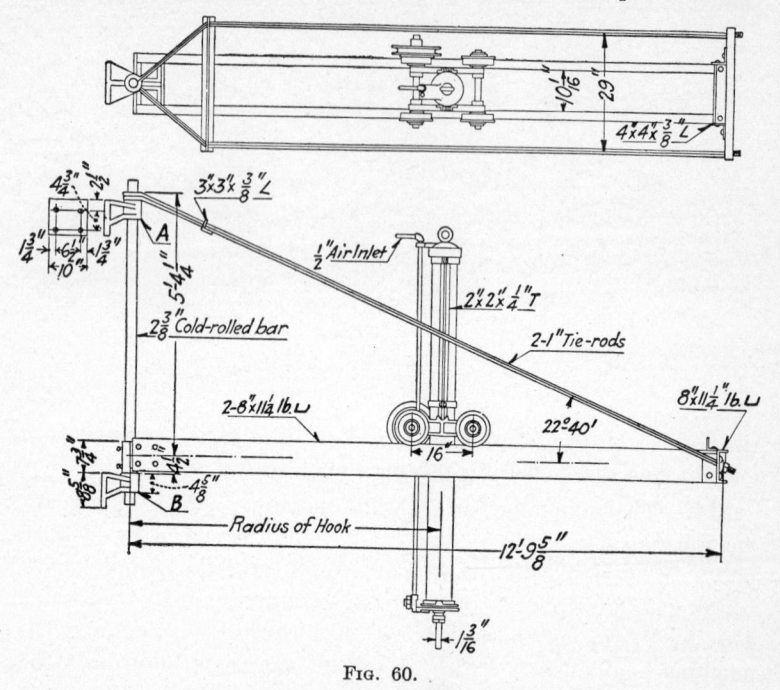

FIG. 60.

crane, when the maximum load is raised. (a) Assuming the efficiency of the air cylinder is 94 per cent., what is the maximum load that can be raised and what are the stresses produced in the cylinder and piston rod by this maximum load? (b) What is the maximum stress in the six $\frac{1}{2}$- by 3-in. machine bolts used for fastening the lower cylinder head? (c) Determine the maximum stress produced in each member of the frame. (d) What are the unit bearing pressures coming upon the supporting bearings A and B? (e) If the bearing A is anchored to the wall by means of four $\frac{7}{8}$-in. machine bolts, what is the maximum stress coming upon each

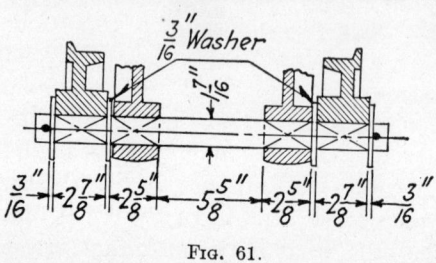

FIG. 61.

of these bolts? (*f*) Determine the maximum bearing pressure and stresses coming upon the trolley axle, a detail of which is shown in Fig. 61. (*g*) What are the maximum stresses produced

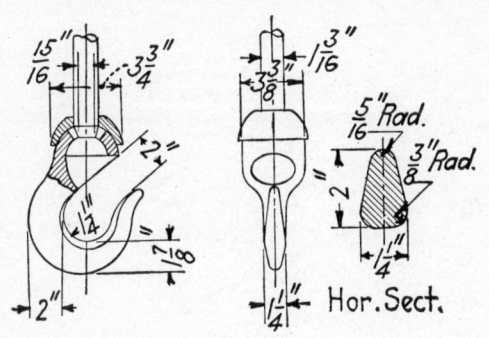

Fig. 62.

in the horizontal section of the hook, as well as in the piston-rod end, having given the dimensions shown in Fig. 62?

514.—The punching and shearing machine, shown in Fig. 63, has a capacity for punching a 2½-in. hole through a ½-in. steel plate. The stroke of the ram is 1¾ in. and the pinion shaft, running at 220 r.p.m., is driven from a countershaft by means of a 4½- by ⅜-in. leather belt laced with rawhide. Assuming the machine is operating at its maximum capacity, determine the following pressures and stresses produced in the various parts of the machine: (*a*) The magnitude of the force *P*, also the bearing, shearing and bending stresses coming upon the crankpin, the proportions of which are shown in Fig. 64. (*b*) The bearing pressure coming upon the front main-shaft journal, the proportions of which are shown in Fig. 64, assuming it takes the entire load *P*. What is the torsional stress in the journal? (*c*) Assuming the efficiency of the mechanism between the punch and the pinion shaft is 88 per cent., what load comes upon the gear teeth? Using Lewis' formula, determine the stresses in the teeth. (*d*) Assuming that each of the six gear arms has a 2¼- by 4½-in. elliptical cross-section at the hub, what is the maximum stress produced in the arms? (*e*) The maximum stresses produced in the main shaft at the back bearing, also at the sections where the diameter of the shaft changes. (*f*) The foot-pounds of work delivered by the belt during the punching cycle, assuming the coefficient of belt friction as 0.35 and the angle of contact on the

Fig. 63.

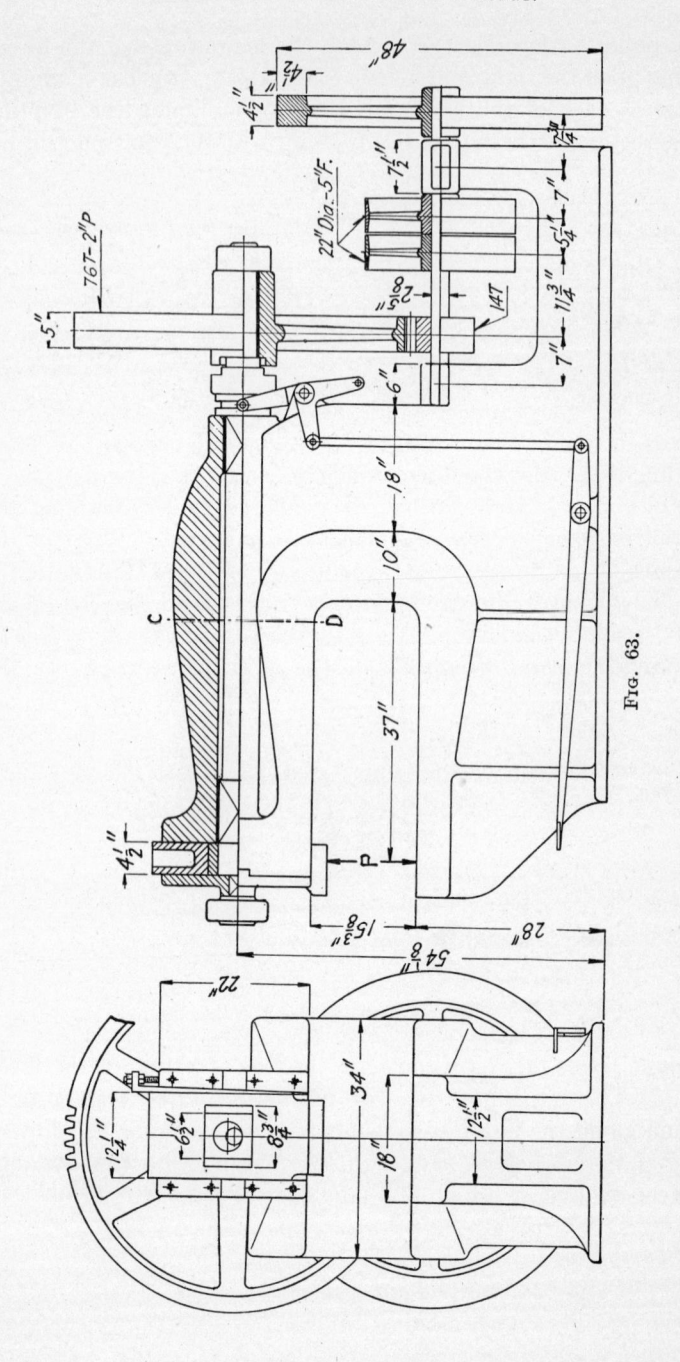

belt pulley as 180 deg. What are the magnitudes of the forces, acting upon the tight pulley, due to the belt? (*g*) The maximum stress in each of the six flywheel arms, assuming the elliptical cross-section at the hub is 1½ by 3 in. At the rim, the arm has

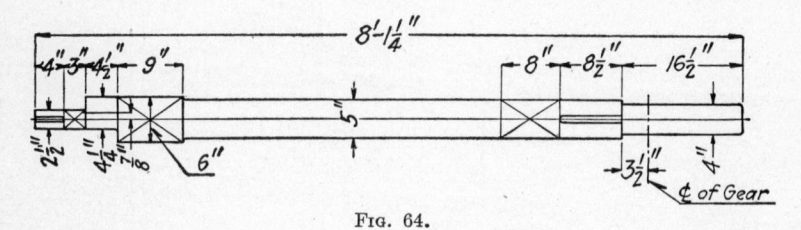

Fig. 64.

a cross-section of 1¼ by 2½ in. (*h*) The weight of the flywheel rim and arms; also the foot-pounds of energy that the flywheel is capable of supplying during the punching cycle, assuming the overall efficiency of the machine as 83 per cent. What is the magnitude of the so-called "coefficient of speed fluctuation?" (*i*) The pressures coming upon the bearings supporting the pinion shaft, also the maximum stress induced in this shaft. (*j*) The maximum stresses produced in the principal section, of the

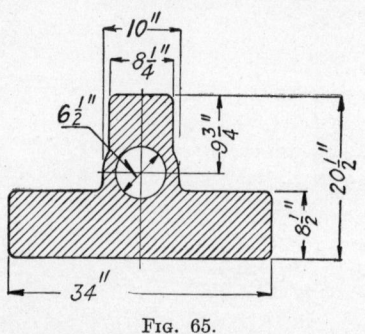

Fig. 65.

machine frame, at right angles to the line of action of the force P. (*k*) The maximum stresses produced in the frame, in a section along the line CD shown in Fig. 63, assuming the dimensions of the section as shown in Fig. 65 and that the distance between the line of action of P and the section CD is 34 in.

SECTION XVI

DESIGN PROBLEMS

A. COMPRESSED-AIR-OPERATED JIB CRANE

The specifications, given below, cover the essential points required for the design of a compressed-air-operated jib crane of the direct-acting type.

Capacity.—The crane must be capable of raising a maximum load of ―― lb. through a height of ―― ft. at a radius of ―― ft.

Cylinder.—The operating cylinder must be made of ―― and have an inside diameter large enough, so that the maximum load may be raised with an air pressure of 100 lb. per square inch. The permissible stress in the cylinder may vary from ―― to ―― lb. per square inch.

Cylinder Heads.—The cylinder heads must be made of cast iron and fastened to the cylinder in such a manner that they may be readily removed for inspection of the cylinder. The permissible stress in the heads may vary from ―― to ―― lb. per square inch.

Piston.—The piston must be made of cast iron and designed to permit the ready renewal of the cup-leather packings. The permissible stress in the piston may vary from ―― to ―― lb. per square inch.

Piston Rod.—The piston rod must be made of cold-rolled steel and at its lower end must be provided with a swivel connection to permit easy manipulation of the hook. The permissible stress in the piston rod may vary from ―― to ―― lb. per square inch.

Hook.—The hook must be made of open-hearth steel and connected to the piston rod by a suitable swivel connection.

Trolley.—The hoisting cylinder must be mounted upon a trolley by means of trunnions so as to permit swinging in a vertical plane. The side frames of the trolley are to be made of steel casting, and the permissible stress therein may vary from ―― to ―― lb. per square inch. The wheels supporting the trolley must be made of cast iron and must be mounted on cold-rolled steel axles fastened rigidly into the side frames. The permissible stress in the axles may vary from ―― to ―― lb. per square inch. The trolley must be provided with a suitable hand-racking mechanism.

Frame.—The main members of the frame, namely, the mast and jib, must be made of standard steel shapes fastened together with rivets. For the braces, standard steel shapes or rods may be used. The upper and lower ends of the mast must be rigidly fastened to suitable members made of steel casting. These mast-end-castings must be provided with well-designed bearings that insure easy rotation and, at the same time, maintain proper alignment of the crane. All bearings must be provided with an effective means of lubrication.

Operating Valve.—A suitable valve for controlling the air supply to the cylinder must be provided. This valve should be so designed that it may be readily dismantled without disturbing the air pipe connections.

Safety Check Valve.—In order to prevent the sudden dropping of the load, due to failure of the air supply, a suitable check valve must be provided in the air line.

Piping and Fittings.—All piping used in connection with the compressed-air cylinder must be of standard weight and all fittings must be made of cast iron.

Problems $A1$ to $A6$.—It is required to design a direct-acting compressed-air-operated jib crane, of the single top-braced type, fulfilling the A specifications given above and using the capacity and general dimensions, given in Table 19, for the particular problem assigned.

TABLE 19

Problem number	$A1$	$A2$	$A3$	$A4$	$A5$
Capacity of crane, pounds	2,000	3,000	4,000	5,000	6,000
Stroke of cylinder, feet			6		
Radius of hook, feet			15		
Lowest position of hook above the floor line, feet			2		
Center line of jib above the floor line, feet			12		
Mast and tie-rod connection above center line of jib, feet			5		

Problems A6 to A11.—It is required to design a direct-acting compressed-air-operated jib crane, of the single under-braced type, fulfilling the A specifications given above, and using the capacity and general dimensions given in Table 20 for the particular problem assigned.

TABLE 20

Problem number	A6	A7	A8	A9	A10
Capacity of crane, pounds	2,000	3,000	4,000	5,000	6,000
Stroke of cylinder, feet			6		
Radius of hook, feet			15		
Lowest position of hook above the floor line, feet			2		
Center line of jib above the floor line, feet			12		
Center line of mast to intersection of jib and brace center lines, feet			9		
Center line of jib to intersection of mast and brace center lines, feet			10.5		

B. HAND-OPERATED JIB CRANE

The following specifications cover the essential points required for the design of a hand-operated jib crane.

Capacity.—The crane must be capable of raising a maximum load of ―― lb. through a height of ―― ft. at a radius of ―― ft.

Power.—The crane must be operated by hand power.

Hoisting-gear.—The hoisting-gear must be built up in the form of a self-contained winch and attached to the frame of the crane at a distance above the floor line, so as to place the crank-shaft at a convenient height for ease of operation. The winch must be provided with two speeds, a slow speed for heavy loads and a fast speed for light loads. All gears must be made of high-grade cast iron and shall be cut from the solid stock, except in the case of shrouded or very large drum gears.

The hoisting drum, made of a good grade of cast iron, must be provided with machined grooves for the extra-flexible steel wire rope with which the crane is to be equipped. The drum must be of ample size to take, without overlapping, the effective length of the rope.

Brake.—The winch must be equipped with a mechanical load brake, which will automatically hold the load upon releasing the operating cranks and permit lowering of the load under the control of the operator.

Trolley.—The side frames of the trolley are to be made of high-grade cast iron, and the permissible stress therein may vary from —— to —— lb. per square inch. The wheels supporting the trolley, must be made of cast iron and must be mounted on cold-rolled steel axles. The permissible stress in the axles may vary from —— to — lb. per square inch. The trolley must be fitted with idler sheaves having turned grooves to insure smooth running of the hoisting rope.

Racking-mechanism.—A suitable mechanism, for moving the trolley back and forth on the jib, must be designed so that it may be operated by means of a pendant hand chain. This mechanism is to consist of cut spur gearing driving a chain sheave, all of which are mounted on a self-contained frame fastened rigidly to the jib members. Proper means for taking up the slack of the racking-chain must be provided.

Hook and Block.—The hook, made of open-hearth steel, must be provided with a suitable shank to permit the use of bronze washers or a ball thrust bearing on the trunnion supporting the hook. The trunnion and the pin carrying the block sheaves, are connected by properly designed steel side-plates. The block sheaves must have turned grooves and must be fitted with bronze bushings or some form of roller bearings.

Frame.—The main members of the frame, namely, the mast and jib, must be made of standard steel shapes fastened together with rivets. For the braces standard steel shapes or rods may be used. The upper and lower ends of the mast must be rigidly fastened to suitable members made of cast iron or steel casting. These mast-end-castings must be provided with well-designed bearings that insure easy rotation and. at the same time, maintain proper alignment of the crane.

General.—All bearings used on the winch, trolley, trolley-racking-mechanism, sheaves, block and mast-end-castings must be provided with an effective means of lubrication.

All cast iron used in the construction of the crane must be free from injurious cold-shuts and blow-holes.

Problems B1 to B6.—It is required to design a hand-operated jib crane, of the single top-braced type, fulfilling the B specifications given above and using the capacity and general dimensions, given in Table 21, for the particular problem assigned.

TABLE 21

Problem number	B1	B2	B3	B4	B5
Capacity of crane, pounds	2,000	3,000	4,000	5,000	6,000
Travel of hook, feet			9		
Radius of hook, feet			15		
Mast and tie-rod connection above center line of jib, feet			5		
Distance from floor to ceiling, feet			18		

Problems B6 to B11.—It is required to design a hand-operated jib crane, of the single under-braced type, fulfilling the B specifications given above and using the capacity and general dimensions, given in Table 22, for the particular problem assigned.

TABLE 22

Problem number	B6	B7	B8	B9	B10
Capacity of crane, pounds	4,000	6,000	8,000	10,000	12,000
Travel of hook, feet			10		
Radius of hook feet			16		
Distance from floor to ceiling, feet			18		

C. HAND-OPERATED PILLAR CRANE

The following specifications cover the essential points required for the design of a hand-operated pillar crane of the fixed-radius type.

Capacity.—The crane must be capable of raising a maximum load of ____ lb. through a height of ____ ft. at a radius of ____ ft.

Power.—The crane must be operated by hand power.

Hoisting-gear.—The hoisting-gear must be built up in the form of a self-contained winch and attached to the frame of the crane at a distance above the floor line, so as to place the crank-shaft at a convenient height for ease of operation. The winch must be provided with two speeds, a slow speed for heavy loads and a fast speed for light loads. All gears must be made of high-grade cast iron and shall be cut from the solid stock, except in the case of shrouded or very large drum gears.

The hoisting drum, made of a good grade of cast iron, must be provided with machined grooves for the extra-flexible steel wire rope with which the crane is to be equipped. The drum must be of ample size to take, without overlapping, the effective length of the rope.

Brake.—The winch must be equipped with a mechanical load brake, which will automatically hold the load upon releasing the operating cranks and permit lowering of the load under the control of the operator.

Hook and Block.—The hook, made of open-hearth steel, must be provided with a suitable shank to permit the use of bronze washers, or a ball thrust bearing on the trunnion supporting the hook. The trunnion and the pin carrying the block sheaves, are connected by properly designed steel side-plates. The block sheaves must have turned grooves and must be fitted with bronze bushings or some form of roller bearings.

Frame.—The boom must be made of standard steel shapes and is to be supported at the top by steel tie-rods that are fastened to a cap-casting located on top of the pillar. The base of the boom is fastened rigidly to a supporting-frame which is fitted with two rollers, running upon a machined surface on the pillar. The boom supporting-frame is held in position on the roller path by steel tie-rods, the upper ends of which are fastened to the cap-casting on top of the pillar. In order to reduce to a minimum, the force required to rotate the crane-frame, the horizontal and vertical loads coming upon the cap-casting must be carried by roller and ball bearings respectively.

Pillar.—The pillar, supporting the crane-frame with its attachments, must be made of high-grade cast iron. A short distance above the base flange, the pillar must be provided with a machined roller-path. Into the top of the pillar must be fitted a steel pin carrying the cap-casting with its bearings.

General.—All bearings used on the winch, sheaves, block, supporting-frame and cap-casting must be provided with an effective means of lubrication.

All cast iron used in the construction of the crane must be free from injurious cold-shuts and blow-holes.

Problems $C1$ **to** $C6$.—It is required to design a hand-operated pillar crane of the fixed-radius type, fulfilling the C specifications given above and using the capacity and general dimensions, given in Table 23, for the particular problem assigned.

TABLE 23

Problem number	$C1$	$C2$	$C3$	$C4$	$C5$
Capacity of crane, pounds	2,000	4,000	8,000	10,000	20,000
Travel of hook, feet			15		
Radius of hook, feet			20		
Approximate distance from ground to cap-casting, feet			9 to 10		

D. PUNCHING AND SHEARING MACHINE

The following specifications cover the essential points required for the design of a belt-driven punching and shearing machine.

Capacity.—The machine must be capable of punching a ——-in. hole in ——-in. mild-steel plate having an ultimate tensile strength of 60,000 lb. per square inch.

Frame.—The main frame of the machine must be made of a good grade of cast iron, free from blow-holes and sponginess, and have a section that will safely withstand all torsional stresses coming upon it, due to the use of cross-shearing tools. The depth of the throat is to be —— in., and the distance from the frame to the ram, when the latter is at the top of its stroke, is to be —— in. The permissible tensile and shearing stresses in the material of the frame may vary from —— to —— lb. per square inch. The permissible compressive stress may vary from four to six times the values given for tension.

Main Shaft.—The main shaft is to be made from an open-hearth steel forging containing from 0.25 to 0.30 per cent. carbon. The crankpin and journals must be of ample proportions to resist safely all stresses coming upon them. All journals on this shaft are to be polished and the keys for the clutch sleeve are to be fitted accurately and held rigidly in place by suitable screws. The main-shaft bearings in the frame are to consist of renewable phosphor-bronze bushings. The permissible stress in the main shaft may vary from ―― to ―― lb. per square inch.

Pendulum.―The pendulum is to be made of steel casting, free from defects and must be fitted accurately to the crankpin and ram. The bearing for the crankpin must be bushed with a good grade of phosphor-bronze. Proper provision for insuring lubrication of all moving parts must be made.

Pendulum Block.―The pendulum block is to be made of a good grade of phosphor-bronze, and have such proportions that it will safely withstand all pressures coming upon it.

Ram.―The ram is to be made of a good grade of cast iron and must be provided with a liberal sliding surface containing oil grooves so as to insure proper lubrication. It must be provided with a bronze gib for taking up any wear that may occur. Means for fastening the punching and shearing tools must also be provided. The stroke of the ram is to be ―― in.

Head-plate.―The head-plate is to be made of a good grade of cast iron, and is to be properly fitted to the main frame. The main shaft bearing in the head-plate is to be bushed with phosphor bronze. The load coming upon this bearing should be transmitted onto the frame through a tongue and groove joint or an enlarged pin, and not through the studs or cap screws used for fastening the head-plate.

Clutch Sleeve.―The clutch sleeve must be of the jaw type, fitted to the main shaft and attached thereto by means of two feather keys. In the case of light machines, the sleeve must be made of cast iron, while for heavy machines, steel casting may be used. The jaws of the clutch sleeve must be fitted with hardened steel faces, in order to reduce the wear coming upon the jaws.

Gearing.―The gear and pinion are to be made of a good grade of cast iron and the teeth must be machine moulded. The gear is to be bushed with phosphor-bronze, and equipped with properly proportioned clutch jaws. If these jaws are cast integral with the gear, the working faces must be provided with hardened steel plates. The velocity ratio of the gearing is to be made 7.5 to 1.

Pinion Shaft.—The pinion shaft is to be made of ordinary cold rolled shafting and provided with liberal bearings, of the split type, lined with a good grade of babbitt metal. The speed of the pinion shaft is to be —— r.p.m. The permissible stress in the shaft may vary from —— to —— lb. per square inch.

Flywheel.—The flywheel is to be made of a good grade of cast iron. Its outside diameter is to be —— in., and its face —— in. The weight of the flywheel must be such that the drop in speed, due to the punching operation, is not excessive.

Pulleys.—The machine is to be equipped with tight and loose pulleys —— in. in diameter and having a face of —— in. The machine is to be driven by a double belt —— in. in width.

Back-stand.—The back-stand, made of a good grade of cast iron, is to be of the same general design as the main frame and fastened thereto by properly fitted machined bolts. The pinion shaft bearing on the back-stand is to be of the split type, lined with a good grade of babbitt metal.

Automatic Stop.—The machine is to be equipped with an adjustable automatic stop, by means of which it is possible to stop the ram at any desired point of its travel.

Treadle.—The treadle is to be of such a design that all lateral springing is reduced to a minimum. All studs, pins, rod-ends and connecting rods and links, used on the treadle and clutch operating mechanism, must be proportioned liberally to withstand hard usage and the resultant wear therefrom.

Counter-balance.—The machine is to be provided with a counter-balance, in order to relieve the crankpin of the pressure due to the weight of the ram, pendulum and tools fastened to the ram. The counter-balance must be made adjustable.

Lubrication.—All bearings throughout the machine are to be provided with an effective means of lubrication.

Double Machine.—In designing a single punching and shearing machine according to the specifications given above, the fact should not be lost sight of, that not infrequently it is desired to make a double machine. This may be accomplished by placing, back to back, two single machines having the same capacity.

Problems $D1$ to $D16$.—It is required to design a belt-driven punching and shearing machine, fulfilling the specifications given above and using the capacity and general data, given in Table 24, for the particular problem assigned.

TABLE 24

Problem number	Capacity for punching	Depth of throat	Distance from frame to ram	Stroke of ram	Flywheel Revolutions per minute	Flywheel Diameter	Flywheel Face	Pulleys Diameter	Pulleys Face	Width of belt
D 1		18								
D 2	⅝ by ⅝	24	9 to 10	1⅛	250	36	4	16	4	3½
D 3		30								
D 4		18								
D 5	¾ by ¾	24	9 to 10	1¼	250	36	4	18	4	3½
D 6		30								
D 7		18								
D 8	⅞ by ⅞	24	9 to 11	1⅜	225	42	5	18	5	4½
D 9		30								
D10		18								
D11	1 by 1	24	9 to 11	1½	225	44	5	22	5	4½
D12		30								
D13		18								
D14	1½ by 1	24	10 to 12	1¾	200	48	5½	22	6	5½
D15		30								

E. FRICTION DRUM HOISTS

Problems $E1$ to $E6$.—Using the data given in Table 25 for the particular problem assigned, it is required to design a friction-drum hoist, direct connected to a squirrel-cage induction motor and capable of handling a load of ―― lb. at a speed of ―― ft. per minute. The motor operates continuously on three-phase, 60-cycle, 220-volt current. The drum should be of ample diameter and length so that at least ―― ft. of 6 by 19 plow-steel rope may be wound upon it without overlapping. The mechanism used for operating the machine must be simple and so arranged that the load is always under full control of the operator.

(a) The following limitations are to be observed in designing the hoist:

1. The frame is to be made of cast iron or built up of structural steel.

2. As far as possible, bearings, shafts and friction gears must be selected from manufacturers catalogs.

128   PROBLEMS IN MACHINE DESIGN

3. The driving friction wheel, whose diameter may vary from 6 to ―― in., must be made of tarred fiber and the driven wheel of cast iron. The velocity ratio of these wheels may vary between ―― to 1 and ―― to 1.

4. A factor of safety of not less than six should be used for the rope.

5. In all shafts, the permissible stress may vary from ―― to ―― lb. per square inch.

6. In gear arms, the permissible stress may vary from ―― to ―― lb. per square inch.

7. In the friction wheel, the permissible stress may vary from ―― to ―― lb. per square inch.

(b) Make a sketch of the proposed design and submit it for discussion and approval. After studying the approved design, prepare in detail, a "method of procedure" to be followed in arriving at the dimensions of the various elements used in the construction of the machine.

(c) All calculations should be made in logical order, in accordance with the "method of procedure" and must be preserved in neat form. Well executed free-hand sketches, showing important details with dimensions, must be incorporated in the calculations.

(d) Determine the probable overall efficiency of the machine proper, assuming the coefficient of journal and tooth friction as 0.06.

(e) Make an assembly drawing showing a plan view and a side elevation. In the plan view show, in section, all parts of the machine between the center lines of the shafts and between the bearings supporting these shafts.

(f) Write a complete specification of the machine as designed.

(g) Determine the probable weight of the machine, with and without the motor.

TABLE 25

Problem number	E1	E2	E3	E4	E5
Capacity of hoist, pounds	1,000	1,500	2,000	2,500	3,000
Rope speed, feet per minute	350	350	300	300	300
Rope capacity of drum, feet	250	250	300	300	300
Diameter of friction pinion, inches	6 to 8	6 to 9	9 to 12	9 to 12	10 to 12
Velocity ratio of friction wheels	4–6 to 1	4–6 to 1	5–6 to 1	5–7 to 1	5–7 to 1

SECTION XVII

TABLES

TABLE 26

Values of $\mu = 0.54 - \dfrac{140}{500 + V}$ at various velocities

V	0	100	200	300	400	500	600	700	800	900	V
0	0.260	0.307	0.340	0.365	0.385	0.400	0.413	0.423	0.432	0.440	0
1,000	0.447	0.453	0.458	0.462	0.466	0.470	0.473	0.476	0.479	0.482	1,000
2,000	0.484	0.486	0.488	0.490	0.492	0.493	0.495	0.496	0.498	0.499	2,000
3,000	0.500	.....	0.502	.....	0.504	.....	0.506	.....	0.508	.....	3,000
4,000	0.509	.....	0.510	.....	0.511	.....	0.513	.....	0.514	.....	4,000
5,000	0.5145	.....	0.5154	.....	0.5163	.....	0.5171	.....	0.5178	.....	5,000

TABLE 27

Values of Y in Lewis' Modified Spur Gear Formula, $W = \dfrac{SfY}{p}$

Number of teeth	Involute 14.5 deg.	Involute 20 deg.	Radial flank	Cycloidal	Number of teeth	Involute 14.5 deg.	Involute 20 deg.	Radial flank	Cycloidal
12	0.2106	0.245	0.1635		40	0.3362	0.412	0.2119	
13	0.2233	0.264	0.1666		45	0.3395	0.421	0.2142	
14	0.2358	0.280	0.1697		50	0.346	0.4276	0.217	
15	0.2454	0.2924	0.1728		55	0.352	0.432	0.2185	
16	0.2547	0.305	0.176		60	0.355	0.437	0.220	
17	0.264	0.314	0.179		65	0.358	0.440	0.221	
18	0.2705	0.324	0.1823		70	0.3598	0.443	0.222	
19	0.277	0.333	0.1855	Same	75	0.3613	0.446	0.2232	Same
20	0.283	0.3395	0.1885	values	80	0.363	0.448	0.2238	values
21	0.2893	0.349	0.1917	as for	90	0.366	0.4525	0.225	as for
22	0.2924	0.3552	0.1933	14.5-deg.	100	0.3678	0.456	0.2262	14.5-deg.
23	0.2957	0.3581	0.1948	involute	120	0.3707	0.459	0.2268	involute
24	0.302	0.3645	0.1964		140	0.374	0.464	0.2275	
26	0.308	0.374	0.1995		160	0.376	0.466	0.2281	
28	0.314	0.3835	0.202		180	0.3778	0.4685	0.2288	
30	0.3174	0.3896	0.2042		200	0.3785	0.470	0.2294	
33	0.324	0.393	0.2065		250	0.3814	0.473	0.2309	
36	0.330	0.406	0.209		300	0.382	0.475	0.2325	
39	0.336	0.410	0.2112		Rack	0.3896	0.484	0.2357	

Table 28

Number of teeth	\(3/4\)	\(5/6\)	\(5/7\)	\(5/8\)	\(7/9\)	\(3/10\)	\(9/11\)	\(10/12\)	\(13/14\)	Number of teeth
12	0.1068	0.0754	0.0698	0.0534	0.0449	0.0377	0.0349	0.0292	0.0241	12
13	0.1121	0.0794	0.0723	0.056	0.0476	0.0397	0.0363	0.0308	0.0251	13
14	0.1173	0.0825	0.0748	0.0586	0.0498	0.0413	0.0377	0.0321	0.0262	14
15	0.1205	0.0849	0.0773	0.0603	0.0516	0.0424	0.0387	0.033	0.027	15
16	0.1247	0.0872	0.0792	0.0624	0.0529	0.0436	0.0398	0.0343	0.0278	16
17	0.1278	0.0896	0.0811	0.0639	0.0543	0.0448	0.0465	0.0349	0.0285	17
18	0.1299	0.092	0.0824	0.065	0.0557	0.046	0.0416	0.0358	0.0291	18
19	0.133	0.0935	0.0836	0.0665	0.057	0.0468	0.0422	0.0365	0.0296	19
20	0.1352	0.0951	0.0849	0.0676	0.0579	0.0476	0.0429	0.0371	0.0301	20
21	0.1372	0.0967	0.0861	0.0686	0.0588	0.0484	0.0436	0.0377	0.0306	21
22	0.1393	0.0982	0.0874	0.0697	0.0597	0.0491	0.044	0.0383	0.0309	22
23	0.1404	0.099	0.0886	0.0702	0.0606	0.0495	0.0447	0.0386	0.0314	23
24	0.1425	0.1005	0.0892	0.0712	0.0612	0.0503	0.045	0.0393	0.0317	24
25	0.1435	0.1013	0.0899	0.0718	0.0619	0.0507	0.0454	0.0396	0.0322	25
26	0.1456	0.1021	0.0912	0.0728	0.0624	0.0511	0.0461	0.0402	0.0325	26
27	0.1467	0.1037	0.0918	0.0734	0.0628	0.0519	0.0464	0.0405	0.0327	27
28	0.1477	0.1044	0.0924	0.0739	0.0633	0.0522	0.0468	0.0409	0.033	28
29	0.1487	0.1052	0.093	0.0744	0.0642	0.0526	0.0471	0.0411	0.0332	29
30	0.1498	0.106	0.0936	0.0749	0.0646	0.0531	0.0475	0.0415	0.0335	30
32	0.1518	0.1076	0.0943	0.076	0.0655	0.0538	0.0478	0.0421	0.034	32
35	0.1539	0.1092	0.0962	0.077	0.0665	0.0546	0.0485	0.0427	0.0346	35
37	0.1561	0.1099	0.0968	0.0781	0.0669	0.055	0.0492	0.0434	0.0348	37
40	0.1582	0.1115	0.098	0.0791	0.0678	0.0558	0.0496	0.044	0.0353	40
45	0.1613	0.1138	0.0999	0.0807	0.0691	0.057	0.0506	0.0446	0.0361	45
50	0.1635	0.1155	0.1011	0.0817	0.070	0.0578	0.0513	0.0453	0.0366	50
55	0.1645	0.117	0.1017	0.0823	0.0709	0.0585	0.052	0.0459	0.0369	55
60	0.1665	0.1178	0.103	0.0833	0.0714	0.0589	0.0524	0.0465	0.0374	60
70	0.1687	0.1202	0.1043	0.0844	0.0722	0.0601	0.053	0.0471	0.038	70
80	0.1708	0.1217	0.1056	0.0854	0.0731	0.0609	0.0538	0.0478	0.0385	80
100	0.1739	0.1241	0.1074	0.087	0.0745	0.0621	0.0544	0.0484	0.0393	100
150	0.178	0.1272	0.1093	0.089	0.0758	0.0636	0.0559	0.0496	0.0403	150
200	0.1801	0.1288	0.1106	0.0901	0.0767	0.0644	0.0566	0.0503	0.0408	200
Rack	0.1875	0.1358	0.1156	0.0938	0.079	0.068	0.0594	0.0528	0.0435	Rack

Values of $p'y$ for Fellows Stub Teeth

TABLE 29

Values of $\dfrac{\pi d^3}{16}$ [d = diameter of shaft]

d	0	1/16	1/8	3/16	1/4	5/16	3/8	7/16	1/2	9/16	5/8	11/16	3/4	13/16	7/8	15/16	d
0	0	0.000048	0.00038	0.0013	0.0031	0.006	0.0104	0.0164	0.0245	0.0349	0.0479	0.0638	0.0828	0.1053	0.1315	0.1618	0
1	0.196	0.236	0.280	0.329	0.384	0.444	0.510	0.583	0.663	0.749	0.843	0.944	1.052	1.169	1.294	1.428	1
2	1.571	1.723	1.884	2.055	2.236	2.428	2.630	2.843	3.068	3.304	3.551	3.811	4.083	4.368	4.666	4.977	2
3	5.301	5.639	5.992	6.359	6.740	7.136	7.548	7.975	8.416	8.877	9.352	9.845	10.35	10.88	11.42	11.99	3
4	12.57	13.16	13.78	14.42	15.07	15.75	16.44	17.16	17.89	18.65	19.42	20.22	21.04	21.88	22.75	23.63	4
5	24.54	25.47	26.43	27.41	28.41	29.44	30.49	31.56	32.66	33.79	34.94	36.12	37.33	38.56	39.82	41.10	5
6	42.41	43.75	45.12	46.51	47.93	49.39	50.87	52.38	53.92	55.49	57.09	58.72	60.38	62.08	63.80	65.56	6
7	67.35		71.02		74.82		78.76		82.83		87.04		91.39		95.89		7
8	100.5		105.3		110.3		115.3		120.6		126.0		131.5		137.3		8
9	143.1		149.2		155.4		161.8		168.3		175.1		182.0		189.1		9
10	196.4		203.8		211.4		219.3		227.3		235.5		243.9		252.5		10
11	261.3		270.3		279.6		289.0		298.6		308.5		318.5		328.8		11
12	339.3		350.0		361.0		372.1		383.5		395.1		407.0		419.1		12
13	431.4		443.9		456.8		469.8		483.1		496.6		510.4		524.5		13
14	538.8		553.3		568.2		583.3		598.6		614.2		630.1		646.3		14
15	662.7		679.4		696.4		713.6		731.2		749.0		767.1		785.6		15

TABLE 30

[Values of $\frac{\pi d^3}{32}$ [d = diameter of shaft]]

d	0	$\frac{1}{16}$	$\frac{1}{8}$	$\frac{3}{16}$	$\frac{1}{4}$	$\frac{5}{16}$	$\frac{3}{8}$	$\frac{7}{16}$	$\frac{1}{2}$	$\frac{9}{16}$	$\frac{5}{8}$	$\frac{11}{16}$	$\frac{3}{4}$	$\frac{13}{16}$	$\frac{7}{8}$	$\frac{15}{16}$	d
0	0	0.000024	0.00019	0.00065	0.00154	0.003	0.0052	0.0082	0.0123	0.0175	0.0239	0.0319	0.0414	0.0527	0.0658	0.0809	0
1	0.098	0.118	0.14	0.164	0.192	0.222	0.255	0.292	0.331	0.375	0.421	0.472	0.526	0.585	0.647	0.714	1
2	0.785	0.862	0.942	1.028	1.118	1.214	1.315	1.422	1.534	1.652	1.776	1.906	2.042	2.184	2.333	2.489	2
3	2.651	2.82	2.996	3.18	3.37	3.568	3.774	3.988	4.208	4.439	4.676	4.923	5.176	5.44	5.712	5.995	3
4	6.283	6.58	6.892	7.21	7.535	7.876	8.220	8.580	8.946	9.326	9.712	10.11	10.52	10.94	11.38	11.82	4
5	12.27	12.74	13.22	13.71	14.20	14.72	15.24	15.73	16.33	16.89	17.42	18.06	18.66	19.28	19.91	20.55	5
6	21.21	21.88	22.56	23.26	23.97	24.70	25.44	26.19	26.96	27.75	28.55	29.36	30.19	31.04	31.90	32.78	6
7	33.68	....	35.51	....	37.41	....	39.38	....	41.42	....	43.52	....	45.70	....	47.95	....	7
8	50.27	....	52.66	....	55.13	....	57.67	....	60.29	....	62.99	....	65.77	....	68.63	....	8
9	71.57	....	74.59	....	77.70	....	80.90	....	84.17	....	87.54	....	90.99	....	94.53	....	9
10	98.18	....	101.9	....	105.7	....	109.6	....	113.6	....	117.8	....	122.0	....	126.3	....	10
11	130.7	....	135.2	....	139.8	....	144.5	....	149.3	....	154.2	....	159.3	....	164.4	....	11
12	169.7	....	175.0	....	180.5	....	186.0	....	191.8	....	197.6	....	203.5	....	209.5	....	12
13	215.7	....	222.0	....	228.4	....	234.9	....	241.6	....	248.3	....	255.2	....	262.2	....	13
14	269.4	....	276.7	....	284.1	....	291.6	....	299.3	....	307.1	....	315.1	....	323.1	....	14
15	331.3	....	339.7	....	348.2	....	356.8	....	365.6	....	374.5	....	383.6	....	392.8	....	15

Table 31

Values of $[0.7k + 1.3\sqrt{k^2 + 1}]$

k	0	0.1	0.2	0.3	0.4	0.5	0.6	0.7	0.8	0.9	k
0	1.3	1.376	1.466	1.567	1.680	1.803	1.936	2.077	2.225	2.379	0
1	2.538	2.703	2.871	3.042	3.217	3.394	3.573	3.754	3.937	4.121	1
2	4.307	4.494	4.682	4.870	5.060	5.250	5.441	5.633	5.825	6.016	2
3	6.211	6.404	6.598	6.793	6.987	7.182	7.377	7.573	7.768	7.964	3
4	8.160	8.356	8.553	8.749	8.946	9.143	9.340	9.537	9.734	9.931	4
5	10.129	10.326	10.524	10.722	10.919	11.117	11.315	11.513	11.711	11.909	5
6	12.107	12.306	12.504	12.703	12.901	13.099	13.298	13.497	13.695	13.894	6
7	14.092	14.291	14.490	14.689	14.887	15.086	15.285	15.484	15.683	15.882	7
8	16.081	16.279	16.489	16.678	16.877	17.076	17.276	17.475	17.674	17.873	8

Table 32

Values of $[0.35k + 0.65\sqrt{k^2 + 1}]$

k	0	0.1	0.2	0.3	0.4	0.5	0.6	0.7	0.8	0.9	k
0	0.65	0.688	0.733	0.784	0.840	0.902	0.968	1.038	1.112	1.19	0
1	1.269	1.351	1.435	1.521	1.608	1.697	1.786	1.877	1.968	2.061	1
2	2.153	2.247	2.341	2.435	2.530	2.625	2.721	2.817	2.913	3.008	2
3	3.106	3.202	3.299	3.396	3.494	3.591	3.689	3.786	3.884	3.982	3
4	4.080	4.178	4.276	4.375	4.473	4.571	4.670	4.768	4.867	4.966	4
5	5.064	5.163	5.262	5.361	5.46	5.559	5.658	5.757	5.856	5.955	5
6	6.054	6.153	6.252	6.351	6.451	6.55	6.649	6.748	6.848	6.947	6
7	7.046	7.146	7.245	7.344	7.444	7.543	7.643	7.742	7.842	7.941	7
8	8.041	8.14	8.245	8.339	8.439	8.538	8.638	8.738	8.837	8.937	8